My Dish Towel Flies at Half-Mast

My Dish Towel
Flies at
Half-Mast

Mary Kuczkir

BALLANTINE BOOKS • NEW YORK

Some of the articles in this volume were previously
published in *The Barnesboro Star,* September 27, 1977
through November 22, 1978.

Manufactured in the United States of America

First Ballantine Books Edition: April 1979

1   2   3   4   5   6   7   8   9   10

Library of Congress Cataloging in Publication Data
Kuczkir, Mary.
    My dish towel flies at half-mast.
    I. Title.
PS3561.U23M9   813'.5'4   78-19624
ISBN 0-345-27857-7

To Miles Ranck, Jr. and *The Barnesboro Star*, without whom this book could never have been written.

Contents

ix

Introduction

The Great Move to Outer Mongolia

I knew my husband, Mike, was up to something when he offered to make dinner. He began the preparations for his culinary, gastronomic, gourmet delight by coating three hot dogs with wiener wrap and tossing them in the oven. My suspicion developed into absolute conviction when he plopped the hot dogs in their crisp little oven-baked coats in front of me and lit the candles with a flick of his Bic.

In a searing, sensuous, passion-filled voice, he said he was moving us from the Big Apple to "The home of the light bulb," or supurbia, as he called it.

"But, darling," I murmured huskily, "I don't want to move to Cleveland, Ohio; besides, I switched from General Electric to Westinghouse."

"Just because they manufacture light bulbs in Cleveland, doesn't mean we're moving there. As usual, you weren't listening. We're not going to Cleveland. I'm transporting all of us to Edison, New Jersey. And," he added, breathing heavily, "I said supurbia, not suburbia. There is a difference. You're going to love Edison. It's forty-two square miles and is shaped like a horseshoe. You'll adore the house; it even has a flagpole by the front door. It's on a one-acre wooded lot, and I put a down payment on it."

"The only people who live in New Jersey are the Mafia," I said, singeing the front of his hair with a candle. "And since we don't have a flag, I can't get too excited over a pole. NO!"

"If you'll stop and think, like I did, you'll realize

1

just how much you owe Thomas Alva Edison. Without him you wouldn't be able to go to the movies or play your stereo. And"—he paused dramatically—"you wouldn't be able to talk on the telephone."

"You forgot the alkaline storage battery," I snarled as I dripped hot wax all over his hands. "I like New York and I'm not leaving!"

"You're just being obstinate," he said, sucking on his burned fingers. "Are you telling me that after everything what's-her-name went through to settle suburbia, you're going to let her down? Was all her pioneer spirit for nothing? Did she face all those hardships and all that suffering to be forgotten so quickly? Why, single-handedly she—"

"Found the septic tank and conquered the car-pool crouch. Well, where is she today? Hiding out, that's where. She gave up!"

"She was the greatest," my husband said reverently. "She's not hiding out, she's resting on her laurels."

I refused to be convinced. I knew what's-her-name wouldn't have given up the land she had tamed if it had been a field of clover.

My husband stated it was time for a new breed to take over. He said we were moving into a sophisticated society that was what's-her-name's legacy to us.

Realizing he was getting nowhere, Mike declared that the only democratic thing to do was to put it to a vote. When the final tally was six to one to stay in the Big Apple, he said the kids were minors and their vote didn't count. The revised tally was one to one.

"Look," I pleaded, "I'll give up the telephone, but I can't give up Saks and Bonwit Teller." I clutched the two squares of plastic to my bosom.

"We'll get a dog," my husband cajoled.

"We have a dog already," I snapped. "I can't believe that you would make me give up Times Square on New Year's and the subway system. You know how I love the Rockettes. I know all about suburbia and what good

2

old what's-her-name went through. Now that they have electricity out there, anything can happen."

"For God's sake, we're only going across the river, not to Outer Mongolia. You'll learn to love it, and remember, we can fly the flag and show everyone how patriotic we are."

"We don't have a flag. Besides, I read an article in the newspaper about a lady who moved to suburbia. It said she never saw a bus for two years, and then she disappeared. No one ever saw her again. We're so used to smog and pollution, we'll die if we move out there!"

Exactly one month later, my Saks and Bonwit Teller charges nothing more than melted curlicues, we set out for New Jersey, with five kids, a dog, a cat without a tail, a hamster named Frizbee, four goldfish in a zip-lock bag, and nine cases of light bulbs as a show of good faith.

"What are you writing?" Mike asked warily.

"From this moment on, I am keeping a record of our new life. When we get to Edison, I'm going to ask the person in charge of Thomas Edison's laboratory to place my journals in a time capsule. When they open it years from now, I want the whole world to know why I gave up glamorous department stores."

"You'll do anything for attention, won't you?" my husband said nastily.

The first entry in my journal read:

My husband is a typical male chauvinist with definite sadistic tendencies. He doesn't really care about electricity; he just wants the flagpole and the one-acre wooded lot and to get his picture in the paper when they have the one-hundred-year celebration in 1979 honoring Thomas Alva Edison.

My second entry read:

It's impossible to win the war against luxury

3

and leisure. It didn't take me very long to sur-
render to that which is commonly referred to as a
better quality of life. Our new house has twelve
rooms and there is not a bulb in sight. What I do
have is a flagpole with a dish towel flying in the
breeze . . . at half-mast.

1

Do You Spell it Suburbia or Supurbia?

On the Street Where You Live

When we decided to live in Edison, I thought no one would ever be able to find me. I looked upon our wooded property as ye olde frontier land, where people square-danced, had quilting bees, and made root beer for entertainment. I also thought I would die of loneliness. Wrong on all counts!

The day after we moved into the new house the doorbell rang and a woman demanded to know how many strings of Christmas lights we had. "Two," I said fearfully, hoping I was giving the right answer. When she didn't look impressed, I followed up with, "I have an extra bag of lights." She sniffed and went home. To this day I don't know if it was the right or wrong answer, but just for spite that year I bought four extra strings of colored lights and festooned our entire front yard.

We were in residence one full week when I was invited to three "intimate dinners" and one orgy. Our sixteen-year-old, Patty, explained what an orgy was and ripped up my R.S.V.P. acceptance. She also recommended I pass on the "intimate dinners."

For a street that isn't even on the map, everyone manages to find his way to David Court. On Mondays, Charlie tempts us with his mother's homemade pies and cakes. Hot on Charlie's heels is Millie and her artificial, homemade dietetic yogurt. Millie says she makes out like a bandit after Charlie's cakes and pies.

On Tuesdays, Sy and his Scissor Shop will sharpen

anything that isn't nailed down. In Sy's wake is ding-dong, guess who's calling.

Wednesday is the day for the Book Mobile with its forty-seven titles (thirty-seven Zane Grey and ten Nancy Drew) to arrive. The Book Mobile is followed by the switch-and-swap teams of the Salvation Army and Goodwill.

On Friday we have Babbette and her Traveling Poodle Shoppe. For three bucks a throw, Babbette will tie a ribbon in any mutt's ear. Trailing Babbette is the local dogcatcher, who has yet to catch an animal. We all know he just comes around for Joan Knight's coffee.

Once in a while we get a few stragglers like someone trying to unload his cemetery plots for quick cash, or a real estate salesman who says he can guarantee three times what you paid originally if you'll just sign on the dotted line. From time to time we have to beat off the tree surgeons who want to show us the sky with the compliments of their chain saws, and the religious consultants who offer a Bible and a glimpse into heaven for twenty-nine dollars and ninety-five cents plus tax.

There is one person who has never found David Court, and that's the meter reader. For twelve years David Court has been getting estimated bills. At Babbette's last dog grooming I waved my bill around and demanded that we sign a petition asking for a meter reader.

"We already have one," Joan said.

"I always thought that was a myth the utility company made up so we would stay home on the twenty-sixth of every month."

"Nope. Roberta Anderson saw him and talked to him. She stopped for gas, and he was in the parking lot reading"—she lowered her voice to a bare whisper—*"Hustler* magazine."

"Oh, my God! What did she say to him?"

"She asked him why none of us ever saw him, and do you know what he answered?" We all waited ex-

pectantly. "He said he was faster than a speeding bullet, stronger than a locomotive, able to leap over tall
buildings in a single bound. He said he was a plane, a
bird, and the meter reader. He claimed he had strange
powers and abilities far greater than those of ordinary
men, and, disguised as a mild-mannered spy for *Hustler* magazine, he fights a never-ending battle to bring
us true and accurate utility bills."

"I don't believe in Superman," I sniffed.

"He would have to be faster than a speeding bullet
to get past my Doberman and my beagle," Paula commented thoughtfully.

"He would have to be stronger than a locomotive to
push open the gate to my yard," Ann noted.

"The only way he could read my meter is if he were
a bird or plane with a telescopic lens that could see
through the curtain on the back door," Joan added.

"It's so logical, what other explanation could there
be?" I said, writing out my check.

The Status Symbol

I told my husband, now that my station in life had im-
proved, I needed a status symbol, a cleaning woman.
He fought me every step of the way and only gave in
when I used every woman's weapon and threatened
the ultimate.

The Domestic Engineer arrived promptly at nine to
be interviewed. Before I could say a word, she presented me with a list of demands typed on lemon-
scented bond paper.

1. Employer must pay Social Security.

2. Cantaloupe for lunch in or out of season.
3. Will not do floors or windows.
4. Will only vacuum with an upright Hoover Cleaner.
5. Time off to watch *Love of Life*.
6. Hour off for lunch. Does not include television time.
7. Hourly wage is three dollars.
8. Will only iron collars and cuffs.

"What about the rest of the shirt?"

"That's not my problem. I just do collars and cuffs. With a jacket and vest on, nobody sees a man's shirt anyway."

"Perhaps you could be more specific. What exactly do you do?"

"I make twin beds, but I won't change the sheets."

"But I have a king-size bed."

"If the sheets aren't too flashy and you pay extra, I might consider it."

"What else?"

"I dust, but if you don't use Old English, I won't be a party to ruining your furniture."

"I'll buy it, I'll buy it. What else do you do?"

"I'll stack the dishes in the dishwasher, but I won't unload."

"I suppose David could do that," I muttered.

"I fold towels, no other laundry."

"I guess Patty could be persuaded to pitch in."

"I'll wipe out the tub and sink, but I won't clean johns."

"If I pay Michael, he might do it. Look, I work a long day. Do you cook? Will you start dinner?"

"Only TV dinners."

"We don't like TV dinners. I was thinking more along the lines of roast, salad, baked potatoes, things like that."

She got up and stared down at me. "You don't want a Domestic Engineer, you want a slave."

"What do they go for?"

9

"You have four kids too many and that dog has to go. I'm allergic."

"What's your feeling about husbands?"

"As long as he's not around when I'm here, he can stay. What did you say you did for a living?"

"I didn't, but now that you ask, I'm a writer."

"Oh, no! Oh, no! I don't work for writers. First thing, you'll be knowing all my secrets and writing about them. A writer," she straightened her back. "Never! You should have told me that when I got here. Now I have to charge you for your interview. That's five dollars."

"How about if I write this up and try to sell it to a magazine? When they pay me, I'll pay you."

She left scorch marks on the carpet in her hasty departure.

It's a Dog's Life

Our entire household was in an uproar the other day when the mail arrived and our dog Sam (short for Samantha) received an invitation to a party.

It took us an hour before we could decide who was supposed to open the invitation. We finally gave it to Sam, who chewed it half to death. Later, with the aid of a magnifying glass, we managed to make out the blurred print.

"Well, who invited her?" my husband asked fretfully.

"Doozie."

"Oh, you mean Paula sent the card."

"If Paula signs her name with a paw print, then

yeah, she signed it. There's a copy of the guest list and the menu. Sam has to R.S.V.P."

"For God's sake, I don't believe this," Mike mumbled as he peered through the magnifying glass. "Jethro, Gypsy, Frolic, Duchess, and Radziwell will be there. Sam's a mutt; she won't know how to act with all those classy dogs."

"Who's going to carry the gift?" David, our youngest child, asked.

"How's she going to get there? It's two blocks away," his brother, Michael, wondered.

"It says the Checkerboard Wagon will pick her up, and there is a do-and-don't gift list of things Doozie does and doesn't need," I said.

"What's she serving?" Patty demanded.

"Cycle One, Two, Three, and Four. The party favors are gumdrops made from liverwurst," my husband snorted.

"That's clever. Now, you really have to admit that's clever." I grinned.

"Who is going to do the R.S.V.P.-ing?" Patty wanted to know.

"What if Sam doesn't want to go?" Mike questioned.

"What do you mean, what if she doesn't want to go? Of course she wants to go. This has got to be a first. I don't know a single other dog in the entire world that has ever been invited to a party."

Sam went to the affair and came home an hour ahead of time with a note and a bag tied around her neck. The note read:

I had a really good time. I ate all my gumdrops and a portion of Cycle Three. I saw two movies with Lassie and Rin Tin Tin. I enjoyed both of them. My dog yummies are in the party bag and are to be eaten after my regular dinner.

"If she had such a good time, how come she came

11

home so early and why does she look so bored?" Mike wondered.

David said it was because the movies were in black and white and Sam is used to color.

Creative Zucchini

There are so many creative people in the world, it makes me sick every time I hear them discuss what their thing is and how they do it with originality.

Some people are creative in the kitchen. As far as I'm concerned, you can't do much with hamburgers and hot dogs except decorate them with parsley and artificial flowers.

Athletes say they are being creative when they jog, run, golf, or play tennis, and then diet through sex. In my opinion, the only thing creative about sports is the outfit the athlete wears. God, can you just imagine the ramifications if a jogger jogged in a tennis outfit? And a golfer would be drummed right off the course if he forgot to put mittens on his clubs.

I heard a rumor going around the other day that the Exxon Corporation loves ingenious people almost as much as Mobil Oil and will give a grant to just about anyone to do anything creative as long as he can spell his name.

Because I'm not a creative person I felt left out. I decided this year that my forte was gardening, and so I started off my vegetable patch with zucchini. Any fool is supposed to be able to plant zucchini and marigolds that will grow. It's what you do with the zucchini afterward that makes you creative. Once it takes over the garden and the lawn and climbs all over the house, you have to become imaginative and decide what to do with it. You can palm it off on your neighbors, sell it under an umbrella at the end of the street, cook it twenty-seven different ways for breakfast, lunch, and dinner, and nibble on it while watching TV. After all that, you still have a ton of the stuff. When I ran out of my thirty fantastic ideas, I just set fire to the whole mess.

My friend next door, who refused to take any of my zucchini because she had twice as much, said, "What you did was the most creative thing I ever heard of."

When my application for a grant from Exxon arrived, I was not in the least surprised to see that it was addressed to Mary Zucchini.

The Yellow Brick Curb

I love supermarkets. They're almost like educational institutions. In a supermarket you can observe the habits of others; you can gripe and bitch to the manager about the high prices and feel you're doing your bit to fight inflation, you can learn all kinds of good things like how they put food coloring in the chopped meat to make it look red; how to watch for a tired cashier so you can palm off your coupons for merchandise you didn't buy, and it is also the perfect place to give others the benefit of your knowledge.

I've noticed that two unacquainted women will speak to each other, or a man will strike up a conversation with a woman he doesn't know, but I've never seen one man talk to another male, who is a stranger, unless a woman is present.

Men watch women punch holes in fruit, shake melons and then do the same thing. If there's another man in eyesight, they just take what they want and go about their business. It must have something to do with women. The manager said he wasn't aware of such the very essence of antics in his store and asked if I would please stop filling up his suggestion box with comments on such matters.

The other day my husband and I were practicing togetherness, so we went to the supermarket for some lettuce. While I was picking off sixteen layers of wilted leaves, a woman and her spouse came up to me and asked directions to the shopping mall.

"Do you want the shopping center with the neon lights in the parking lot or the one that has the gigantic L'eggs display at the entrance?"

"I want the one that has the discount store. You know, where they cut out the labels."

"I know the one you mean. There's a florist next door to it that has Boston ferns in the window."

"That's the one. Can you tell me how to get there from here?"

"Sure. When you exit the parking lot, bear to the left till you come to a blue house that has a weeping willow tree at the end of the driveway. Make a right and follow that road till you come to the A & P, then turn left. Make another quick right at the next corner; there's a gas station on one corner and a pizza parlor on the other. Stay on that road till you see Spence's Soccer Sellar and make a right. Keep a sharp eye out for Spence's because he has a shrub that almost covers half the sign. If you miss it, watch for the Burger King and make a left and backtrack. From Spence's, all the way to the shopping center there's a yellow curb. Just follow it, and it will take you right into the parking lot of the shopping center."

"Sounds as simple as abc. Thanks a lot."

14

My husband, who got tired of watching me improve the produce because he said it embarrassed him, looked at the man and proceeded to give *him* directions. "If you want to go to Timberwoods Mall, stay on Melrose till you get to Twenty-seven and turn right. You'll be going south on Twenty-seven. Continue till you come to the second traffic light at Cooper Avenue. Make a left onto Chandler, go two blocks, and turn right at the first light onto Warwick. Follow Warwick for exactly one mile and make another right at the caution light, onto Hoover, and it will lead you into the shopping center. A right, a left, and two rights."

"Simple as abc. Thanks a lot," the woman's husband said.

"He may have all the rights and lefts, but he'll never remember the landmarks," the wife whispered. "Every time we go somewhere he gets lost."

"Just follow the yellow brick curb and you'll get there. Listen, if I give you my telephone number, will you call me if the florist has any ferns on sale?"

"Sure," the woman said as her husband dragged her out the door.

Danger and Intrigue!

When the bell pealed on the small island on David Court, every woman dropped what she was doing and ran.

It was Joan who called the meeting. She assumed her military stance and looked at us with the light of battle in her eyes. "This is it!" she cried. "This is the end! We've lived in fear too long and it has to stop. I

refuse," she yelled, shaking her fist in the air, "to be intimidated. I refuse to keep pulling my shades and drapes and living by flashlight. I want to see the sun. I want to be able to go outside and not have to look over my shoulder. I want my kids to know that fresh air and people live outside and that it isn't a myth. I want the coercion, the threats, the trickery and bribery to stop. We have to take a stand and do something! No more ding-dong, guess who's calling!"

"You're right," we all chorused. "But what can we

16

do? Every time we come up with a plan she outwits us."

"How did it happen? Where did we go wrong?" someone wailed.

"I'll tell you!" Paula screamed. "I know when and how it started, and we have our own greed to blame. If we hadn't gone to her garage sale, we would be free women."

"But nothing cost a cent," Ann reminded us.

"Exactly! And when we left, our arms full of her junk, she was marking down the value of everything we took. She's good till the locusts get here," I shrilled.

"But it was worthless," Roberta insisted.

"Her cosmetics aren't any good. It's junk versus junk," Paula noted with profound insight.

"When we blocked off the street, she came by moped. When we lowered the chain, she came through the yard on foot. When we set the dogs on her, she just happened to have her poodle with her who was in season. Now, that's sneaky," Joan acknowledged.

"We did manage to get our licks in," Ann observed. "Eileen pushed her in the pool."

"Some licks," Joan snorted. "It just proved her stuff is waterproof."

"Now that she's got to the kids, we have to do something," Paula ranted. "I refuse to buy thirty-two dollars and fifty cents worth of cosmetics so my kid can get an Adidas sweat shirt."

"My son said he was going to run away from home if I didn't get the sweat bands," Ann whined in despair.

Joan, who never goes anywhere without her bayonet, thrust it into the ground and announced that this was *war!* "No way am I buying ninety dollars worth of make-up I don't need so my kid can get French-made sneakers. God, they told me she's switching to Puma next week. We have to call the police!"

"We can't. She hangs out in the station's lobby on Tuesdays. This is Tuesday," Eileen cried.

"A trap! We'll set a trap!"

17

"We already tried that. When the snare lifted her off the ground, something went wrong and she went through Paula's window. How much do you still have to work off, Paula?"

"My life," Paula answered dejectedly.

"We'll kill her and bury the body," Ann shouted.

"It won't work; the smell would give it away. We have to adjourn till we can come up with a solution that is foolproof," Joan said.

The Suburban Sophisticate

It's hard to be sophisticated when you're uncoordinated and something of a klutz. I can spot a pothole fifty feet away and still manage to step in it. I could never learn to play the piano or knit, because both took concentration and two hands. However, I can walk and chew gum at the same time.

Obviously, I lack that special quality that will forever bar me from the world of glamour. Although this was quite apparent to me, I did not know what sophistication really was nor is there anyone I'm acquainted with who seems to have this elusive characteristic. The dictionary's definition is confusing so I asked several people, more worldly than myself, if they could give me some tips on how to recognize such a person should I ever see one.

My friend Joan told me to look for a woman wearing sunglasses on top of her head and who had the first three buttons of her blouse open. I didn't have the heart to tell her that wearing sunglasses on top of your head was passé, and now you hook them in the gap made by those three open buttons.

My daughter who thinks she knows everything said a sophisticated person is one who wears sixteen layers of gauze, has two pierced earrings in each lobe, and can recognize the sound of Fleetwood Mac. I wanted to tell her all those layers of thin material that she pays scandalous amounts of money for are the same kind of cloth my mother used to use to strain grapes when she made jelly. But I didn't. As for those two holes in each ear, if God wanted you to have more, he would have given them to you at birth. She had me on Fleetwood Mac, though. I thought it was a Cadillac.

A militant neighbor said being sophisticated was giving up reading Phyllis Schlafly a year ago and still wanting to kill her. This same woman also said sophistication was being able to eat in a restaurant that is so dark you have to flick your cigarette lighter to see your food.

I thought you were sophisticated when the suntan on the front of your legs matched the tan on the back, or admitting you watch the Hardy Boys on television.

My mother, who is a real zinger, said it was having the guts to put copies of *The Dieter's Guide to Weight Loss During Sex* and *How to Flatten Your Stomach* on your coffee table for the neighbors to see. I'm no fool; I burned all my copies of *National Geographic* and ran to the bookstore.

Money is the Name of the Game

When you live in suburbia, it seems like you're fair game for anyone who has a gripe. Legal suits are forever pending and money is the name of the game; someone else's money.

Just the other day I overheard a woman threaten to sue a supermarket. She was yelling to one and all that the shopping carts were stuck together with Krazy glue and someone was going to pay for her wrenched back.

When I stopped at the gas station, a guard dog lifted his leg on a whitewall tire that belonged to a Mercedes. (No class distinction there.) The owner of the automobile threatened to bring action unless he got a complete carwash. "And throw in a lube job for mental anguish," he snapped.

In the post office an irate man was threatening to file suit if they didn't stop delivering junk mail to his house. He then dumped three lawn bags full of the stuff on the counter, telling the postmaster he could take them home with him. "You'll hear from my attorney! Every damn bureaucrat in this country needs to be taken to court!"

A neighbor was running up the street, shouting hysterically that she was going to sue the house painter. It seems he painted the front and sides pale blue, then switched to gray in the back, saying no one would notice. "My husband noticed!" she shrieked.

Back home, I opened my own mail and found a letter from an attorney informing me I was being sued by the United Parcel man because my dog had bitten him on the ankle. It went on to state his client had suffered untold anguish, sleepless nights, time off from work, and loss of services. The bottom line said eighteen-hundred dollars would make it all come out right.

"What does that mean?" I asked Mike. "Are loss of work and loss of services different?" My husband said it was a lot different.

"Are you saying that loss of services means . . ." My husband nodded. "But the dog bit him on the ankle! Oh, my God!" I shouted. "He can't . . . He doesn't . . . That's unheard of! He's lying!"

"Prove it!"

"But what does . . . *that* . . . have to do with an ankle bite?"

"Money is the name of the game," Mike said.

Tolerance

When I moved to what I laughingly call the boondocks, I found there were many things I had to be tolerant about, and one of them was the paperboy. My first encounter with a daily newsboy was with a kid named Jack, who was as big as a defense player for the Green Bay Packers.

Mike, who is more tolerant than I, didn't seem to mind when I had to use your more basic survival methods and sheer guts to retrieve our paper from the television antenna or the telephone wires. While Jack was as huge as a linebacker, he also had a throwing arm equal to that of Tom Seaver.

My husband, who also has a fear of heights, watched me from time to time as I applied silly putty to the end of the broom handle to rescue our paper from inside the chimney. He was happy (my husband) as long as he got the paper on Friday, when Jack collected. He said it was a summary of the week's news and what more could anyone ask for.

When Jack went off to college (with my tips), the paper route was turned over to a young man named Willy, who didn't believe in delivering in the rain or snow. He did, however, force himself to collect in inclement weather. When Willy departed to pursue a higher education (with my tips), he turned the route over to his younger brother, Jerry, who also didn't believe in delivering in the rain and snow and who, according to my kids, also had tired blood. When Jerry

got to our street, he stood at the end and whistled. If our dog wasn't out, we didn't get a paper.

When Jerry went off to college (with the aid of a student loan and a swift kick from his father), we didn't have a paperboy for two weeks.

Eventually a man drove up and pitched the paper in the direction of the house. He lasted till he developed bursitis, or for two weeks, if you were counting by the day.

In desperation the neighbors took turns Xeroxing the news at the library.

With the coming of the weekly papers at the local supermarkets, the newspaper ran an all-out campaign for newsboys. One such reliable person turned out to be a wispy little kid who pulled his papers around in a wagon. He didn't have much going for him except a beautiful smile and a willingness to toss the paper in every puddle he saw, no matter how small it was. The beautiful smile turned into a snarl if his tip wasn't what he expected. He lasted three months and retired to a weekly route.

Our next self-employed youngster worked with his five-year-old sister. He carried the papers on his back and his sister threw them in the bushes. When the sister got a better offer from the child with the enchanting smile, he gave up on the route.

The next entry into the job race was a kid who put notices in our mailboxes, saying he was self-employed and he had bills and obligations that had to be met, and please leave money in plain brown wrappers. This same kid sent us all Christmas cards with his name embossed in gold on the upper left-hand corner. He gave up the route the day after Christmas and retired to Florida with his parents.

We were back to Xeroxing the news when a paper person arrived on the scene. Not only did our paper person wear eye makeup and dangling earrings, our papers were actually in the mailbox. If that wasn't enough to startle us, she offered helpful household hints three times a week as a sideline. Every afternoon, promptly at three o'clock, she arrives on her moped and waits for every eligible boy on the street to run out and fight over who will deliver the papers. She smiles coyly at the winner and does tricks on her moped for the losers.

Quotable Quotes

Little League is great as long as the coaches remember it's just a game and it isn't important if you win or lose, but how you play.

The following are some famous last words of bygone coaches.

"I need you on second. You'll get a body cast after the game."

"Forget the pain. You got to first."

"I want to see that kid's birth certificate after the game!"

"What do you expect from a team whose coaches are a mortician and a pathologist!"

"You would think a twenty-run lead was sufficient."

"The pitcher has to leave now; his taxi is waiting."

"With zero on his shirt I knew he would slide into first."

"I told you at the beginning of the game the umpire was a manic depressive."

"You can't bench that kid; he has pilonidal cysts."

"So what if it's raining. Use your backstroke going into third."

"One more error and you kids get chicken soup in the water bucket."

24

"Either you muzzle those mothers or I quit!"

"The rule book says, and I quote: 'Ten-year-old kids do not have the right to impeach the coach.' "

And then there was Reverend Weaver, who was new to Little League. He protested a call to the umpire by saying, "Poo on your call, Ump." When the umpire got down on his knees and begged for forgiveness, the entire team cheered the reverend.

The Best Seller

Mike settled himself in front of my typewriter and announced that he was going to write a book. An exposé, a runaway best seller, he said, a look of horror on his face.

"I hardly think an exposé of our sex life will be a runaway best seller," I sniffed.

"That's been overdone," he said, fitting the paper into the machine.

"Don't you mean underdone? Or how about non-existent?"

He ignored me. "Two hours in the supermarket, and I have enough material to send every housewife in this development away for ten years! Two hours. What goes on the other ten hours they're open? You wouldn't believe the corruption, the thievery, the larceny, and the assault and battery that persist in a supermarket." Supurbia, he declared, was just riddled with crooks.

"Listen, I'm a straight arrow. I never did an illegal thing in my life."

He said a crook is a crook is a crook.

"What did you see?" I asked fearfully.

"I saw," Mike began, pursing his mouth into a round O of disapproval, "a woman punch a hole in a cantaloupe and just leave it there."

"That was her way of getting back at the produce manager for putting oil on the cucumbers. The sign says glossy cucumbers. Same thing with the apples. The sign says shimmering, glistening scarlet apples. They put wax on the apples, and that's why they glisten and shimmer. Tit for tat."

"What about the lady who stuck her finger in the yogurt and then closed the container?"

"End of the dairy aisle, top shelf, one of each flavor, right? Somebody ripped off the plastic spoons. Those are samples; you're supposed to taste them. Unsanitary, but hardly criminal."

"What about the woman who poked a hole in a detergent box to see if there was a dish towel in it? When the soap spilled all over her groceries, she just left the cart in the middle of the aisle and said she wasn't buying that mess."

"That's one for your side. What else?"

"I overheard two women discussing how they dupe their husbands with Sara Lee cakes and pies. They tell their spouses they stood over a hot oven all day. That's disgusting."

"The word is 'clever.' I've been duping you for years. You hate frozen vegetables, so I just cook them till all the color leaves and tell you they're canned. That hardly makes me a crook."

"It's worth your life to live in this house," he mumbled. "You're as bad as the lady who gave her kid a doughnut from the box and closed the lid? She didn't even look over her shoulder to see if anyone was watching. Crooked and brazen."

"Hold it, now you're attacking motherhood. Top shelf of the bread aisle, facing the plant hangers, is a section reserved for mothers with crying, whiny kids. There's a box of cakes and doughnuts for samples. The sign must have fallen down."

"What about the mother who kicked the stockboy when he told her he was out of Fruit Loops?"

"God, I would have done the same thing. Can you just picture what this house would be like in the morning if David didn't have his favorite cereal? I rest my case."

"Maybe I need to do a little more research."

"You could take a crack at that exposé on our nonexistent sex life. Research is the key to everything.

The Town Ordinance

Edison, like most towns, has a town ordinance that says all dogs have to be leashed.

Cindy woke me one morning at seven-thirty and told me she couldn't get out the front door because nine dogs were guarding the entrance.

"Then go out the back door," I grumbled sleepily.

"I'll miss my train," she yelled. "And I can't go out the back because there are five dogs leaning against the storm door."

"We never had this problem when we were encased in concrete and steel back in our old apartment in New York," I complained as I held open the window for my husband and kids to exit.

I spent the entire day running back and forth between the two doors laying down newspapers.

Weary to the point of exhaustion, I threw a bunch of pork chops into the broiler and promptly forgot about them as I rushed to let someone in the window.

Suddenly an ear-piercing sound ripped through the house. "Oh, my God, it's an air raid! Everyone into the shelter!" I screeched as I raced back to let my husband in.

"Mom, we don't have a shelter!" Michael yelled.

"Right! Right! Everyone into the bathtub and pull the shower curtain!" I bellowed, to be heard above the high-pitched shriek that seemed to be coming from everywhere.

"It's the smoke alarms," my husband shouted as he turned off the broiler.

"Everyone out of the bathtub," I called.

"Open the windows, pry open the doors," Mike continued to shout.

"No! No! Don't open the doors," I shrilled over the wailing alarms. "Don't open the doors!"

"How do you think you're going to get rid of this smoke?" My husband grimaced as he furiously fanned a gray cloud in the kitchen.

"The dog is in heat. Why do you think everyone has been coming and going through the window?"

"I thought the doors were stuck," Mike answered.

"You're too late, Mom, David already opened the door," Michael yelled as he jumped on a kitchen chair to get out of the way of the rushing animals.

"There's an ordinance that says all dogs have to be leashed," I cried hysterically.

"They were," my husband said, pointing to the broken chains and frayed ropes that trailed on the carpet from the circling dogs.

"What are we going to do?" I asked as I eyed Sam who was sitting primly in the middle of the living room, the dogs circling her and trying to nip at her ears.

"Wait," Mike suggested nonchalantly.

"For twenty-one days?" I demanded incredulously.

"Call the police," Michael said.

"Call the vet," David said.

"Give them the pork chops," my husband said.

I called the police and asked for a Swat Team. I got a cop with a partner who was allergic to dogs. The two paragons of law and order viewed the situation through binoculars from a position across the street. Then they blew a whistle to get our attention and advised us to move out.

The vet arrived, surveyed the scene, and said it would cost two hundred dollars to sedate the dogs.

Mike, who was eating a pork chop, told the man he didn't have two hundred dollars.

The vet went home.

The two-man Swat Team said they had to leave because there was a group of kids pelting passing motorists with crab apples and they had to apprehend the lot of them to set an example.

"Leave us a grenade," I begged.

The Swat Team ignored me.

Sam sneezed and went to sleep in the middle of the floor.

"When is she going to do something?" my husband demanded as he tossed his bone into the middle of the circling males.

Sam woke up, ate the bone, and went back to sleep. I shrugged.

"She probably has a headache and her back hurts," Mike answered himself as he ate the last pork chop.

Progress

Progress is something a lot of people look forward to, while others look at it as something you have to live with. I, for one, find it a definite challenge.

In the old days when you got up in the morning and planned your day, you could almost count for every minute. Now a simple little trip to the shopping center is a major event that has to be organized days ahead of time.

A visit to the bank to transact a little business is definitely considered a major event. A bank is a place that you enter via the front door and then walk through a jungle, run between waterfalls, and fight your way to the moving stair that will hopefully take you to where they keep the money, only to find out you have to weave your way through the obstacle course of free gifts for new depositors and displays of English china.

If you should find that you need gas, you're in big trouble if you missed the free course in the park on how to pump gas at the new self-service gas stations. I was the last one in town to learn that gas goes under the license plate.

And if a trip to the supermarket is on your agenda,

you can count on at least three hours to padiddle your time away. If you can manage to find your way through the stacks and displays of lawn chairs or to scoot between the potted plants and hanging baskets, you just might end up in the clothing aisle, where you can buy Fruit of the Loom underwear in a variety of sizes. If you want to buy something so mundane as food, you have to pick up the phone at the end of the aisle and ask for what you want. Someone will come and get you, after you give him your exact location, and escort you to the item of your choice. If you need more than three items, you have to start out the night before.

One rainy day I made the mistake of going to the market for some hamburger, but all I could find were umbrellas, plastic raincoats, boots, and colorful totes.

When I complained to the manager, he said we live in a nation of fat people and that his store was doing everything in its power to alleviate the problem. He said this was called progress.

2

The Human Factor

Would You Believe...

Society wouldn't be able to survive without excuses. The theme today, especially among children, seems to be, Why take the rap when you can blame it on someone else?

Mom, would you believe I didn't rip my new pants. When I was coming home from school, Sam was so glad to see me she jumped up on my leg and tore a hole in the knee.

Smoking? Me? Would you believe that on the way home I had to run through a smoking pile of leaves on the road. If I detoured, I would have been late to take out the trash.

What hole in the wall? A squirrel got into the house and tried to chew her way out.

The tulips? Do we have tulips? Oh, those tulips! Mrs. Knight's cat ate them. I even watched her get sick—the cat, not Mrs. Knight.

The vase? The dog's tail knocked it over. I guess she was standing on the chair. Somebody must have tied a battery to her tail.

I did rake the leaves. Those leaves are from the Witt's trees. Their leaves are orange; ours were all brown.

I can't even pronounce Givaund, so why would I use your perfume?

I'm not little; I just have short legs.

Mom, tell them I don't wear braces, tell them this is a Halston necklace that I clasped too high.

One of my favorites is an excuse I heard my nephew

Ricky give his mother after his first encounter with a six-pack. "But, Mom, you know I'm too young to drink. The guy at the pizza parlor thought he was being funny, and he put hashish on top of the pie."

Perfection!

People are always saying they have a perfect child, a perfect husband, a perfect marriage, a perfect this or a perfect that.

Webster defines perfect as flawless, without defect.

I'm married with a husband and five kids, and there isn't a perfect one in the bunch.

What I do have is a twenty-four-year-old hypochondriac, a twenty-one-year-old rights and cause person (she'll picket and protest anything within a thirty-mile radius as long as she doesn't have to make the sign), a sixteen-year-old sex symbol (voted so by her class) who doubles as a consumer activist after school, a thirteen-year-old Little League athlete who knits afghans and has a waiting list of nine customers, and a ten-year-old who thinks there are only four words in the English language: lift up the seat!

Perfect husbands do not have receding hairlines, hemorrhoids, paunches, bunions, or flat feet. I don't have one; a perfect husband, that is.

I do have an almost perfect dog.

There aren't too many people who can boast that their dog can sit on top of the piano and watch the leaves blow.

She guards the bathroom door when someone is taking a bath. (The lock is broken.)

You only have to tell her three times to eat her Gravy Train.

When she's told to put her toys back in the box, she woofs once, picks up one toy, and then goes to sleep.

She knows how to take the keys out of my handbag so I'll take her for a ride. She's partial to the gas station, and the boy on duty gives her gumdrops.

She pays attention to me when I read her my articles. She never yawns till she's back in her basket.

She knows how to straighten the bedspread with her teeth after she gets off the bed so no one will know where she napped.

Right or wrong, whoever appears to be getting the short end of the stick, she's right there offering her belly to be scratched.

She's not perfect, she's not even a pedigree. She's just a little mutt someone let loose in the parking lot of the supermarket. She is loyal and she is affectionate, just like all those nonperfect people who walk around and through our lives.

The Game Plan

With four females in our house, we have the guys slightly outnumbered when it comes to bathroom use. There is not a patient or a forgiving one in the bunch (males, that is). They simply refuse to understand things like: false eyelashes take time to glue into place; bubble baths aren't something you hop in and out of in a couple of minutes; unless one takes one's time shaving one's legs, they could be full of nicks and scratches; and blow drying is something you have to work at.

"This is it!" the three male chauvinists cried in unison the other morning. "We timed the lot of you, and from now on we have a new game plan."

"Cindy took forty minutes, Patty thirty-five minutes, Susy forty-three, and you," Mike said, fixing his steely gaze on me, "took fifty-four minutes! That's a total of two hours and fifty-two minutes, or one hour and fifty-two minutes more than it should——."

"I can't hold it any longer!" David interrupted. "I have to go!"

"Don't let him in there! He's the one who never lifts the seat!" Cindy screamed as she tried to block the door.

"That's because I don't have time!" he shouted, scooting under her arm.

"From now on you each get fifteen minutes, and anyone who goes over his limit gets the water turned off. Michael is monitor."

"I can't shave my legs and blow-dry my hair in fifteen minutes. There won't be any time left for make-up," Patty squealed.

"Tough. When you're ugly nothing helps," Michael commented coldly.

"But it takes half an hour just to take a bubble bath. If I use up my time, I won't be able to put in my contacts," Susy grumbled.

"It's either-or. Take your choice," Michael said callously.

"It takes me fifteen minutes just to put on my eyelashes," Cindy complained.

"So do it the night before and you'll have extra time. Fifteen minutes is all you're getting."

"And you," my husband said, zeroing in on me. "A quarter of an hour, that's it!"

"I need every one of those fifty-two minutes. Do you have any idea what I would look like without my avocado facial? It also takes careful attention to iron out your wrinkles. And then I have to wait ten minutes for my Line Tamer to work. Everyone of my thirteen freckles have to be bleached separately. Maybe fifty minutes, but that's it."

Michael's no fool; he knows where his allowance comes from and who chauffeurs him here and there. "She's right, Dad. Let's give her the fifty minutes, and if she can't get a handle on it, we'll build another bathroom," he said magnanimously.

We're Grown Up!

Between serving the mashed potatoes and the pot roast, I made my announcement. "I'm running away from home!"

From my husband: "Don't charge anything. Should I set the alarm?"

"Holiday Inns prefer charge cards, and what difference does it make if you set the alarm or not? You always sleep through it anyway."

From Michael: "Can I go, and can I bring my friend Matt?"

"No, you can't bring Matt, because you aren't going with me. Last week Matt's mother ran away and she didn't take you."

From Dave: "Will you make my bed and wash my sweat suit before you leave?"

"Make your own bed, and I just washed your sweat suit last month. Run the hose over it."

From Patty: "You promised to bake sixty-four cupcakes for Carol's sweet-sixteen party. It's my contribution."

38

"The only thing I'm contributing to Carol's party are the baking instructions on the oven door."

From Cynthia: "Can't you wait till next week? You promised to go with me while I have my corns removed."

"No one, to my knowledge, has ever died from corn removal. Wing it."

From Susy: "You said you would help me make drapes for my room."

"Dye some sheets and you won't have to sew at all."

So much for lasting relationships.

Not to be outdone, the dog dragged her leash over to me and laid it on my lap.

"How come you're taking Sam?" Mike asked.

"For protection, and she keeps her mouth shut."

"I hope she gets carsick," David said.

"Isn't anyone going to ask why I'm leaving? Isn't anyone going to plead and cry and beg me to stay?" I moaned wretchedly.

In unison they chorused, "If you want to be childish, go ahead. We're grown up!"

3

It's Tuff to be a Kid

The Black Cloud

Sometimes, like at dinner, I feel as though I'm living under a black cloud.

One of Dave's friends, who stops by for supper on a regular basis, says dinnertime at our house is like *The Gong Show* and wants to come by more often.

From Mike: "Either you feed those kids first or I'm eating out. We can do without your famous meat loaf from now on."

That's just for starters.

Me: "For the last time, David, there is no fat in meat loaf. Stop picking."

Me: "Michael, there is no skin on meat loaf. Either you eat it or I'll stuff it down your throat."

Me: "Patty, stop mashing. The meat has already been ground. If you don't eat it, you get it for breakfast."

Me: "Cindy, this is the last time I'm going to tell you that's not a bone around the edge, it's a firm crust."

Michael: "Whose turn is it to do the dishes?"

Patty: "Well, it isn't mine. I did them last night. We had pork chops and I had to clean the broiler."

Michael: "I did them the night before when we had stewed tomatoes and nobody ate any."

David: "Just because I'm the smallest doesn't mean you're sticking them with me."

Michael: "Mom, tell him to stop breathing on me! Make the little twerp do them; he never does anything but eat and leave a mess."

Cindy: "Don't look at me. I work all day."

David: "Yeah, don't look at her. She's so ugly the dishes will crack if she does them. Cindy never does anything except look at herself in the mirror. Buy Joy, Mom, so she can see herself in the plates, and maybe then she'll do them. Everyone picks on me."

Cindy: "Mom, get this turkey off my back before I kill him."

Me: "I have a brilliant idea," I whispered. (In our house the only way to get anyone's attention is to whisper. They think they might miss something if they didn't listen.) "Let's all agree in silent sign language who is going to do the dishes, because if you don't, we're having meat loaf four more nights this week."

If one had a mind to, one could write a book on togetherness.

Like Mother, Like Daughter

There's an old saying that goes, "Like mother, like daughter." Sometimes it applies to me and sometimes it doesn't.

Mom always said you could tell the way a woman kept house by the condition of her butter dish and ketchup bottle. Needless to say, she had a covered butter dish, and the neck of her ketchup bottle was crystal clear. My butter dish (a saucer) has toast crumbs and jelly around the edges, and my ketchup bottle defies description. Once I yelled at Patty to clean it. When I saw her lick off the excess ketchup, I gave up. I never fight a losing battle.

When I was growing up, you did the laundry on Monday and hung it outside so the neighbors could see

43

how white your whites were. The underwear was hung between the sheets or on a line that couldn't be seen from the street. In those days everyone knew you wore underwear, you just weren't supposed to advertise it. Now when I hang out clothes (when the dryer is broken), I make sure that everyone can see my unmentionables. God forbid they should think I don't wear any.

Mom really had this thing about these intimate pieces of apparel. Every time we left the house she would march us back in to check our underwear, her theory being that we might be in an accident and get taken to the hospital. I tried that on my kids and got nowhere. I finally figured I was ahead of the game last year when I convinced them they had to change every day.

Constantly, Mom would threaten me for sucking my thumb. One day she put the fear of God into me by saying she was going to snatch me baldheaded while I slept. I decided to spring that trick on Michael a couple of years ago, and he said, and I quote: "Go ahead. You'll have the only baldheaded ten-year-old in captivity."

There were other things I learned at my mother's knee, like how to pass off Heloise's hints as my own without batting an eyelash. If I'm having guests for dinner and by some chance serving meat loaf, I tell everyone I use ground round when it's really regular beef with twenty-six percent fat content. I also learned how to apply Mop and Glo and pretend I spent the day scrubbing and waxing. The knack to this, according to good old Mom, is to rub an emery board over your knees so they'll look red and puffy.

I knew my kids were too smart to fall for it, but I tried to palm off liver on them by telling them it was soft steak, like Mom used to do to me. All I can say is, you win a few and you lose a few.

When I used to sound my battle cry of "There's nothing to do, No one to play with, I'm hungry," ten times a day, Mom would tell me to play in the attic by myself and that there were corn flakes in the pantry. I tried running that one by my kids, but they weren't buying. Somehow I ended up taking them to the movies and McDonald's. They really got to me when they said they would be midget Quasimodos if they played in the crawl space that was our attic.

When I grumble to my mother about the way things work out, she tells me to get it in gear and stop whining.

Dear Parent/Guardian

The letter addressed to the Parent/Guardian of Patricia Ann arrived in the morning mail. After twenty-four years one would think the school system knew my name. Right off, that letter ruined my day and set me nuts.

The letter was short, curt, terse. My presence was requested in the vice-principal's office an hour before the beginning of Parent Night to discuss the actions of one offspring of said Parent/Guardian.

Posthaste and forthwith, I immediately sat down and penned off a sixteen-page missive informing the vice-principal of my estimated time of departure and arrival.

By my best calculations school had been in session exactly twenty-six days, and already I had been summoned to the vice-principal's office three times.

The first time I was informed that Patricia Ann had deliberately, with malice aforethought, crushed a four-ounce empty milk carton beneath her Adidas sneaker.

I agreed with the vice-principal that this was indeed earth-shattering as I slinked my way out of his paneled office that smelled like oregano.

The second time I was told by the vice-principal in no uncertain terms that he could not condone, sanction, or forgive Patricia's blatant disregard for the gym rules. "Green knee socks are totally unacceptable," he said in a horrified voice.

"The hot-water heater broke, white clothes have to be washed in hot water, colors in cold, fine washables in lukewarm, in All-Temperature-Cheer," I babbled as he escorted me from the office, the blackboard pointer stabbing me in the back.

My third visit to the oak-paneled office was even more horrendous. In a tone I recognized from the mortuary, I was apprised that this time Patricia Ann was in "big trouble." She wrote and passed not one but two notes to a classmate during Science class. "A boy!" he said in hushed tones.

"Oh, my God!" I responded, properly shocked. "What did it say?" I whispered.

"It said," he replied solemnly, "that she would not do his crummy homework because he was a crummy person and she didn't need his crummy Stevie Wonder album, and not even for his crummy Beach Boys album, either, would she do his crummy homework."

If I had a tail it would have been between my legs when I exited the herb-scented office, the crummy note clutched in my crummy hand.

Parent Night arrived all too soon to suit me. Just as I was leaving, my son Michael told me to be sure to stop in his room first so I could read his paper entitled "Parents." Pure blind panic washed over me. Last year, after one of Michael's papers, the Child Neglect Center paid me a two-hour visit. My husband told me to pull up my socks and get going. I went.

The literary masterpiece was hanging on a wire with a clothespin and was done in purple ink.

46

MY MOM

My mom is kind of special. My dad says she is "different," but I think she is special. She never dresses up like the other mothers. My mom wears sneakers and blue jeans and she can outrun a skunk on a cloudy day.

When we go off to camp she tells us not to hurry home, and if we break any bones, to set them ourselves or the counselors won't let us come back next year.

My mom covered up my chicken pox with her dark makeup so I could play in the last football game. She told the coach we just came back from Florida. She sent presents and get-well cards to all the other players.

When my sisters go out on dates, my mom checks the gas tank and kicks the tires. Sometimes she checks the trunk, too.

My mom is cool. She calls my friend Matt a turkey. She said he was the pits and the least he could do was go home every two weeks and bring back a clean towel. When my mom took me and Matt and Scott camping, she lost Matt and Scott. She left without them. She said if they were dumb enough to get lost, they were dumb enough to find their way home. Matt said my mom is a turkey and he isn't going camping with her any more. My mom told him to put it in writing.

MY DAD

My dad is kind of special, too. He fixes our bikes, and when they don't work he takes them to the bike shop. He shares everything with us. When he got a new lawn mower, he gave us all three free turns. When he gets his new leaf raker, he's going to share that with us, too. My mom said his middle name is "Share." When my dad takes us fishing, he lets us gut the fish and cut off the heads. If we don't catch any fish, he tells Mom we had a flat tire and had to come home.

My friends' fathers all look at the pictures in *Playboy*. Not my dad! He reads the articles. My mom told him to pick one and tell her what it was about. He said he couldn't, because they were all good.

Instead of going on to the vice-principal's office, I decided to go home and clean the house for the Child Neglect people. Besides, my socks were falling down again and I didn't feel like pulling them up.

You'll Never Miss Them!

When the pediatrician told David he had to have his tonsils out, said son and his mother became hysterical.

"You'll never miss them! I've taken out hundreds of tonsils. Just think, no more sore throats," the doctor cajoled.

"Sure, sure. I go into the hospital to have my tonsils out and somebody takes my kidneys and heart. I saw that movie *Coma*," Dave muttered ominously.

"That's make-believe. This is real," the doctor informed him reassuringly.

"Oh, yeah? Try telling that to the guy who went into the hospital for a simple knee operation and ended up dead. Now tell me this is real," my son said, running from the office.

"I saw the movie, too," I whispered. "He's too little

for someone to steal his kidneys. They aren't even fully grown."

"I don't believe this," the doctor remarked huffily.

"You should; one of your colleagues wrote the book," I retorted just as huffily.

"But it's fiction."

"Prove it."

"I don't want his kidneys, I want his tonsils."

"What are you going to do with them?" I demanded.

"Study them and tell you why he's been getting so many sore throats."

"But if you take his tonsils, he won't be able to talk and cry out when they try to take his kidneys," I bleated. "Besides, he has a fear of heights, and all those wires will cut into his skin. No tonsils and no kidneys," I said firmly.

Four house calls, nine telephone conversations, and three consultations later, my son agreed to the operation as long as the doctor met his demands.

Round-the-clock nurses.

A signed affidavit from the surgeon that he would remove only the tonsils and nothing else.

That he could wear a whistle around his neck whose sound would carry to the waiting room.

A cop on duty outside the operating-room door.

Eight-by-ten glossies of his entire blemish-free body, to be taken before the operation.

The pediatrician signed in triplicate and the operation was on.

Dave came home from the hospital with his kidneys intact, his tonsils in a jar, and a police escort.

Sugar and Spice

In my opinion, there was nothing more earth-shattering than the day Michael brought home his first girlfriend . . . at the ripe old age of thirteen and a half.

"The girl hasn't been born who's good enough for him. I wanted to be the one to pick out his first girlfriend. It's my inalienable right as a mother," I cried wretchedly to my husband.

"You're projecting again. He's got a good ten years before he makes a commitment. She looks like a nice sugar-and-spice girl," Mike observed.

"Girls are tricky, wily, and devious, and let's not forget foxy. He won't have a prayer; he's our slow one."

"Is it okay if Kimberly stays for dinner?" Michael asked, a stupid look on his face.

"I thought I told you never to bring anyone home when we're having pork chops," I hissed.

"She can have mine," our son said magnanimously.

"See! See! Already he's sacrificing. Today he's giving her his food. God only knows what it will be tomorrow."

"Kimberly is Jewish, and they don't have pork chops in her house."

"What do you mean she's Jewish!"

"It's okay, Mom. Her mother is having a fit, too."

I jabbed my husband in the ribs. "Did you hear that? Her mother is having a fit. I'm not having a fit. Do you think I'm having a fit? Why does he think I'm having a fit?"

"If you want a haphazard guess, I'd say it's because you took off your Saint Christopher medal and draped it around his neck. I'm sure she's a lovely girl. Look how protective she is of Michael."

"She's clutching him."

"What time is dinner, Mom?"

"Six. Why?"

"I have to take Kimberly home at six-thirty because I'm taking Michelle to the soccer game."

"But you're giving her your pork chops. I thought—"

"Mom, she's only my girlfriend for dinner. Can I bring Angela home on Wednesday? She loves spaghetti."

"Give me back my medal! Anyone who can juggle three females is on his own!"

Can't Wait Till I Leave Home!

I think every mother has at one time or another heard these famous words, "I can't wait till I'm eighteen so I can leave home and be on my own."

Those words were my twenty-four-year-old's battle cry for seven years. The day she turned eighteen she trenched in, and I've been stuck with her ever since.

52

I might have had a chance of unloading her, but somewhere between twenty and twenty-one, she turned into a hypochondriac.

On your average day she comes down with at least five illnesses. Recently, at seven-thirty in the morning she came down with diverticulitis, hives, and suspicious lumps on her legs, and her hair was falling out.

By sundown the lumps moved to her jaw, her hives developed pimples, and her falling hair broke into split ends. The diverticulitis was dormant but could flare up at any given moment, she said.

Good mother that I am, I rushed her to the pediatrician (she said his opinion was the only one she would respect) and told him she had everything but the heartbreak of psoriasis. The doctor prescribed bed rest and orange juice and said she would live.

On the drive home I tried to point out that it was time she got married and left home now that she was affianced, although, I noted, sotto voce, "Al looks like he's dragging his feet lately." I could have saved my breath because it was like beating a dead horse.

Since I didn't seem to be getting anywhere with Cindy, I decided to approach the object of her affections directly. Al said he didn't think she would hold up over the long haul. I assured him the pediatrician said she only needed a little TLC. He looked doubtful, even a little suspicious.

"Look," I cried wretchedly, "I'll pay for the marriage license, the honeymoon, and a trip to the Mayo Clinic if you'll just set the date."

I told myself I couldn't let him get away. I knew, the minute I saw the way he hemmed his pants with a staple gun, that he was the one for Cindy. If that didn't convince me, I was certain when I saw him pour melted butter and Ragu over my spaghetti and then make a sandwich out of it.

When I drilled him the second time, he mentioned he wanted to see how she kept her room before he made a decision. "Oh, God," I dithered, "pick something else. The only time we get to see the inside of her room is on Christmas Eve, when she opens the door to throw out her presents."

When Al's hair started to fall out and he developed a twitch in his left eye, not to mention a medically diagnosed ulcer, they set the date for their marriage. Al said he was sick of spaghetti and Ragu, and didn't I know how to cook anything else? "Besides," he mumbled ominously, "the doctor said spaghetti and Ragu would kill me."

Everyone was ecstatic over the good news. Susy was beside herself as she pried the nails from the windows Cindy had hammered shut to keep out the fresh air. Patty was elated that the medicine cabinet would now have room for her toothbrush. Michael claimed her dessert for the first year. David placed a large red X on her door to stake out his claim to her room.

My husband said he would divorce me if I told Al the only thing Cindy knew how to cook was spaghetti and Ragu.

I'm on Top

When I went to school, if you did something wrong you "caught it" from the principal and then you "got it" again when you went home. Today it seems to be a little different. Actually, it's a lot different.

Yesterday the junior-high-school principal called and said I was to come to school with my husband. He said Patricia had a slight altercation.

"What does a slight altercation mean?" I demanded.

"It means Patricia got knocked around and is sitting in my office." As an afterthought, he let us know she was all right.

"Well," Mike said irritably.

"It's fairly simple. Patricia was walking through the hall on her way to class—incidentally, she was not at fault—when a student tripped her and then kicked her as she started to get up. The turkey said she was on his turf and he decked her. When she said he was the living pits, he decked her again. Patricia got up with the aid of a couple of derfs and gave him a chop to the neck, and it was a burnout. Girls shouldn't fight," the principal said virtuously.

"The name, give me the name," I said firmly.

"I'm on top of this."

My husband, who was sitting with a puzzled look on his face, wanted to know what language the principal was speaking.

"English. Every mother in this school is bilingual; where have you been?"

Patty spoke up. "It was an emotionally disturbed minority student."

Her father said, "Huh?"

"I'm on top of this," the principal repeated. "Patricia's teeth will be fixed."

"What's wrong with her teeth?" I screamed.

"They're chipped, is what they are, but I'm on top of this."

"Oh, my God," my husband groaned. "Two thousand three hundred dollars for orthodontics, and he tells me he's on top of it!"

Patty asked who was going to pay for the twenty-five-dollar chain she bought with her baby-sitting money, and what about her ripped shirt?

Mike said, "Oh, God!"

"Get an estimate on her teeth and bring it in," the principal suggested.

"Patty, why is your mouth bleeding?" I asked.

"Because my tongue keeps hitting the chipped teeth."

"You said we were going to get a fair trial," my husband hissed.

"We are. He wants an estimate on her teeth."

"About this emotionally disturbed student," Mike continued.

"I'm on top of this. There's no cause for worry."

"When you get there, what are you going to do?" my husband demanded.

The principal said, "Huh?

"I want you to take Patricia home and let her finish out the day watching television so she'll calm down. She's not being suspended, since she didn't start the altercation, but I do wish you would tell her that girls don't fight."

"What did Patty do, exactly?" Mike questioned.

"She might have three chipped teeth, a lacerated tongue, a broken chain, and a ripped sweater, but she won. When she got up she threw the turkey, and he landed against the wall. He has a sore groin and a broken arm. The turkeys call it survival of the fittest."

"What does that mean?" my husband whispered.

"It means those thirty-dollar-a-month karate lessons helped your kid break another kid's arm that doesn't belong to this school."

The Tangible Evidence

The other day I was sitting outside reading my mail when a neighbor pulled into her driveway, crying and shouting hysterically. I stopped what I was doing and watched one very subdued kid exit the car behind his shrieking mother.

When the woman spotted me, she ran over and thrust a paper under my nose. "Read this! You're a writer—read this, just read it!"

Being as smart and astute as I am, I immediately figured out that since this was the last day of summer school, the kid had goofed and flunked, and she wanted me to see the tangible evidence.

"Look, it's not the end of the world. So you'll get him a tutor during August and he'll still make it." I squinted at the paper and saw a bright red A in the corner. "What's your problem? The kid got an A."

"Read it!" she bellowed. "The title says it all!"

HOW TO GLUE, PASTE, STICK, AND PIN YOURSELF TOGETHER IN THE MORNING—AND IF YOU BOTCH THE JOB, CALL ELIZABETH ARDEN FOR A MIRACLE.

"Kill him!" I screamed.

"This was one of those read-aloud things with a demonstration," my neighbor cried as she collapsed on the driveway. "He got an A in content, an F in grammar, and an A plus for the demonstration!" she said, and banged her head on the blacktop.

"You're going to have to lock him up for the rest of his life. You know that, don't you?" I yelled. "It's kids like yours who give every mother in town a bad name. The whole world will know what we do in the morning."

"Now I know why he's been lurking outside the bathroom door and scribbling in his notebook," she cried wretchedly.

"And he's only seven and a half," I said in awe. "He'll be a menace by the time he's grown."

"He'll never reach maturity!"

The Middle Kid

A middle kid, to hear him tell it, leads the life of a drudge, is put upon unmercifully, and is hated by everyone, even the dog.

While Susy was growing up, she led me a merry chase. When it was time to clean her room, I would hear, "You hate me. That's why you're making me clean this stinking room."

"No," I would demur, "it's because you are the one who made it stink, and I have a sensitive nose."

"You hate me, everyone hates me. You didn't want me!"

In my best motherly voice I would say, "Of course I wanted you. I still want you, but you're cleaning this room!"

"Oh, no, if you really wanted me, you would have had me first. All I ever get is leftovers. Leftover this and leftover that. Everybody hates me!"

"For instance?" I asked wearily.

"I'll make a list. It's too long to go into right now. Now I have to play Cinderella! I hate Cindy's leftovers. She hates me, too. She hated me from the day I was born!"

"That's not fair. She was only two years old when you were born, so how could she hate you?"

"You used her old diapers and her bibs with the spinach stains on them for me."

"That's because we were too poor to buy new ones."

"Sure, sure, but you weren't too poor to buy them for her. That's some of the leftovers. Admit it, you always liked her best. I'm the middle one. Everyone hates the middle one. You like Patty and the boys better, I can tell. You never make them clean their rooms."

"That's because they majored in neatness and their rooms don't smell. Clean it!"

"What will you give me if I clean it?"

"A swift kick if you don't. Now start cleaning!"

"You're always picking on me. Pick, pick, pick. You watch, I'm going to be the one who never amounts to anything, and it will be your fault because you don't love me. You always buy toys for the boys' birthdays, and you buy me underwear."

"The boys are still little, and you always need underwear when your birthday comes up. Don't forget, I always take you to the movies and out to dinner."

"That doesn't count. I hate wrapped underwear."

"So next year I'll give it to you in a paper bag. Now clean!"

"Do you really love me?"

"You bet."

4

The Number One Lady in Town

It's Time for Little League, or My Mother Will be Glad to Do It

With sixteen children eligible for Little League, David Court was well represented at the April 12 meeting of the Edison Little League. It wasn't till April 13 that I heard the good news. My son Michael, according to the Little League president, said, and I quote: "My mom will be glad to do it." End of quote.

"It" turned out to be coaching eighteen Pee Wees who were on a waiting list. When the Little League president expressed some doubt over Michael's generosity, said son followed up with, "She's better than nothing." The president affirmed this was indeed true and agreed to make me coach of the Pee Wees.

My knowledge of baseball was limited. I knew if you hit the ball you ran, if you missed the ball you sat down. With this in mind I called an emergency meeting of the Busy Bees and drafted all the girls. Joan, who had been in the army for five years prior to her marriage, said that calisthenics was the answer. Laura noted she hated to wear cleats and also had serious doubts about wearing a baggy sweat suit. Paula told us her head would perspire if she had to wear a billed cap.

My son, the one who volunteered me, stripped a banana and stuffed it in his mouth as he handed me a list of the kids and a rule book.

I cried. Smedzinasky, Jacsinowsky, Bubeckiskzy, Kalowotosky, Goldberg, Asimovitchzi, Radomodosky, Petrushevich, Szatamatowicz, Hrynkiewicz, Smith, Im-

pellizeri, Matuskiewicz, Osofosky, Rosenbloom, Besely-Bendix, Caudericciz, and Fortoloczki.

Mike laughed hysterically when Michael informed him of my new position. He laughed all night while I read the rule book. He was still laughing when I brushed my teeth before bed. He lost fifteen pounds. The doctor said this happened because the wires in his jaw only allowed him to take liquids.

The following day my assistants, eighteen Pee Wees, and I took to the field.

"They're babies," I moaned.

"They should be in a sandbox," Paula cried.

"They should be home watching cartoons," Laura said indignantly.

"They should be clutched to their mothers' bosoms," Ann wailed.

"Calisthenics is the answer," Joan decreed.

"Okay," I yelled as I blew my whistle for attention. "Hear this! All thumb suckers stand over here, all bladder problems over there. All pigeon toes and knock knees stand by home plate." There was a mad scramble as all the Pee Wees assumed new positions.

"All lefties go to second and all braces go to third. Hold it, this isn't going to work," I screamed as a bladder went to a leftie and a thumb sucker joined the braces.

"What's your problem, Jacsinowsky?"

"I'm a thumb sucker and pigeon-toed, but my knees don't knock. Where should I go?"

"Home," I muttered through clenched teeth.

"Calisthenics is the answer," Joan noted knowledgeably.

"There's a solution, we just have to find it. Paula, take notes.

"All thumb suckers go to the outfield. All bladder problems go to first base and right field; you'll be closer to the bathrooms. Pigeon toes play shortstop."

"We have two pigeon toes that have a bladder problem," Paula cried wretchedly.

"I have to stand in the grass," Szatamatowicz yelled. "I'm not allowed to get my new cleats dirty."

"Mark that down, Paula."

"Can I go to the bathroom?" Besely-Bendix asked.

"You said you were a thumb sucker," I said petulantly.

"I am, but I still have to go. My mother made me drink two glasses of water before I left so if I sweat I wouldn't lose all my body fluids."

"Mark that down, Paula."

"Calisthenics is the answer," Joan cried.

"We're going to scrimmage. We'll divide the players and make two teams. Joan, you take one team and I'll take the other. Laura, you umpire home plate. Ann, you coach second base, and Paula will keep the records. Joan's team is the Busy Bees and mine is the Willing Workers.

"Shut up and let's PLAY BALL!"

"I don't want to be a Willing Worker," Fortoloczki yelled.

"You're going to love it. Get out in the field and suck your thumb. Not another word! Move!"

"When I go home, I'm gonna tell my mother," Fortoloczki cried between his braces and thumb.

"Calisthenics is the answer," Joan told us yet again.

The Busy Bees were up at bat and the Willing Workers took to the field. The top of the first inning took an hour while we all looked for a foul ball.

"This is a wooden bat," Matuskiewicz complained. "My mother only lets me play with a whiffle bat made out of plastic."

"Shut up, Matuskiewicz, and hit the ball. You have to take your thumb out of your mouth when you hold the bat," I shrieked through clenched teeth. "No, Matuskiewicz, you don't swing till the pitcher throws the ball!

"What do you mean, that's a strike?" I yelled at the umpire. "The pitcher knocked out the overhead light."

"Okay, foul ball," Laura acquiesced.

"You're going the wrong way, Goldberg. You're supposed to run to first, not third. I don't care if you're tired or not. You have to go to first, then second, and then third."

"He's safe," Laura yelled from behind home plate.

"Time," Ann called from her position at second. "I just want to know one thing. Is he safe on third or is he safe on first?"

"I think he quit and went home," Paula said, making a note in her record book.

"If he comes back, we'll compromise and put him on second," Ann suggested. We all agreed.

"PLAY BALL!

"Caudericciz, you're up at bat. What are you waiting for, a bus? Hustle, hustle. You're not chopping wood; swing out, not up.

"Joan, how come the catcher keeps missing the ball?"

"Because he only weighs forty pounds and he's wearing forty-five pounds of equipment. I told you—"

"Calisthenics was the answer."

"When are we going to eat the cupcakes?" Osofosky called from left field.

"What cupcakes?"

"Today is my birthday and I brought cupcakes."

"We're going to eat them right now, Osofosky. Did you bring candles?"

We played twenty-one games and lost twenty. I still don't know how we won the one we did. Joan said it was because Goldberg ran to third after he hit the ball and no one noticed.

Infinite Wisdom

According to my kids, a mother is supposed to be an authority on everything. Personally, I like to pass the buck once in a while. Unfortunately, there isn't anyone to pass it to, so I have to sink or swim on my own.

When our oldest daughter was little, she wanted to know why she needed a bellybutton. Cindy was happy when I told her some sheik might gift her with a ruby someday and that's where she could safely keep it.

When Dave was six, he wanted to know if angels wore white suits with zippers, and did they come in husky and slim? (He's my smart one.) I said yes.

Around the same time Michael wanted to know why birds flew south in the winter. When I told him the planes were overbooked, he didn't question me at all.

Susy wanted to know what a beer belly was. She trusted my suggestion so completely (that all she needed to do was look at her father), that she asked Mike to stand up.

At age eight, Cindy wanted to know what thunder

was. God blowing bubble gum, I muttered. She didn't ask for clarification.

Once in a while you win one like "Why do I have to brush my teeth?"

"Because I'm your mother and I said to brush them."

"Why was George Washington the father of our country instead of someone else?"

"Actually, Betsy Ross was supposed to be the mother of our country, but she was busy sewing the flag, so they gave the job to George." I'll admit the kid looked skeptical, but he didn't pursue the matter.

When tales of my infinite wisdom reached the four-year-old next door, he asked me why fish swim. When I told him it was impossible to walk on water, he said he didn't know fish had legs.

I just call them like I see them, I told him.

Euphoric Bliss

My husband said everyone who is sophisticated goes camping. I tried to argue the point, but I didn't get very far. He said it was the "in" thing to do. I pleaded and cried for a pop-up or a camper, but Mike replied that was for the non-"in" crowd. He then purchased a tent and all the equipment necessary to be "with it." That was four years ago.

Happiness is tent camping on your vacation.

Euphoric rapture is living with eight other people and two dogs in a seven-man tent for two weeks.

Mind-boggling ecstasy is being confined to a tent while a summer storm rages for four days.

Total joyous enchantment is sloshing down the road in hip boots to go to the bathroom.

"It's that time of year again," my husband chirped from behind his newspaper.

I scurried to the desk and withdrew a folded piece of paper, duly notarized, that said this year we were going on a vacation like other people. "I want to fly Eileen to some exotic place south of the border and stay in a motel," I said in a quivering voice. My husband was quick to point out that this was entirely selfish on my part.

I retaliated by telling him my poor arthritic body couldn't take the dampness of the woods and that sleeping bags were not conducive to good health. He replied that air conditioning and luxury living were killers and that Eileen only went to Florida.

I told him I would settle for Joe Zilch and his crop-dusting plane if I could stay in a motel. For my efforts I got a thirty-minute dissertation on the merits of fresh air, clean water without chlorine, trees, and open fires, including the reason why motels don't allow dogs.

Poor sport that I am, I stomped my way to the attic.

I wished for a flood, a minor earthquake, transmission trouble. I also wished for a temporary prostate condition for you-know-who. "I'll settle for a good case of infectious diarrhea," I muttered as I threw down the tent stakes.

It was not to be.

I wanted to choke the life from Grizzly Adams, my husband's idol, as I scrunched myself next to the dog in the car. The kids were fighting and swatting one another with double Oreo cookies as Sam leaped over the seat for the crumbs.

You-know-who settled himself into the driver's seat and immediately burst into "Off We Go Into the Wild Blue Yonder." And that was exactly where he belonged, a lead weight tied to each foot, I thought nastily.

I prayed steadily for a full hour that Big Bird would descend and snatch him baldheaded.

Nothing happened.

Nine hours later we arrived at a campground called Camper's Heaven. Seeing no heavenly attire, angels, or harps, I immediately demanded that my husband ask for a refund.

We didn't get one. Big Bird still hadn't arrived.

Everybody took off to view the sunset over the lake.

I pitched the tent.

After I cooked the dinner and after I did the dishes, everybody went to the recreation hall to try out the pinball machines.

I unloaded the car.

While everyone toasted marshmallows and had a sing-along, I blew up the four-man rubber boat.

When I collapsed at twenty-two minutes after midnight, my husband told me to relax.

Four days later, at three-fifteen in the morning, I stopped the car at the entrance to the campground and watched six ladies change the name of the sign. It now read Camper's Hell.

All of us flew Mary Ann to Guadalajara and eight glorious days of poolside service, soft music, and gourmet cuisine.

I got back to Camper's Heaven, or Camper's Hell, depending on your point of view, just in time to take down the tent, load the car, and deflate the boat.

Stop, I Say, Stop or Else...

Have you ever noticed the way a mother will do just about anything she's asked if it concerns kids? I haven't figured out if it's a question of survival or a call to arms. Probably survival; otherwise how could we live with our whiny children?

Pat called me the other day and asked me to substitute for her on her crossing-guard job. "Is it hard?" I asked.

"No, you just stand there and blow a whistle. I'll bring the stuff right over."

"What stuff?" I was becoming suspicious. "I have a whistle."

"You have to wear a suit and carry a STOP sign."

"What kind of suit and how big is the sign?"

"The suit is sort of a one-piece, iridescent, orange jumpsuit. It's made out of plastic, so don't smoke when you're wearing it."

"What will happen if I do?" I asked curiously. "Don't you have any other colors? Orange clashes with my red hair."

"They only come in orange, and don't worry about your hair, you have to wear an orange iridescent hat. You'll go up in flames," she said, answering the first part of my question. "Haven't you ever seen a crossing guard?"

"Not in years. My kids take a bus. Will the hat burn, too?" I inquired fearfully.

"Usually it's the first to go. I'll be right over with the stuff. I guess I better bring the mask, too, just in case the kind your kids have is wrong," my friend said happily.

"What mask? You didn't say anything about a mask!"

"It's a guard mask, the kind the football players wear. You have to wear it to protect your face."

"Why?" I demanded.

"Because sometimes the little darlings throw tomatoes and rotten apples at you. I'll bring the whistle, too, since it's specially made."

"Why?"

"Because the sound carries for great distances. If you're standing in the middle of the road and a big truck comes barreling along you have to blow the whistle so the guard at the next stop can alert the police. It's easy."

"Do I really have to stand in the middle of the road? Why can't I stand on the side?"

"I don't know," my friend answered. "When I was hired, they told me I had to wear an orange suit and stand in the middle of the road. Cars won't hit you if you're wearing an orange suit."

"And you get paid for doing this!" I gasped in amazement.

The following morning, promptly at eight o'clock, I assumed my position in the middle of the intersection closest to my friend's school. I tested out the whistle, and fourteen dogs and two cats surrounded me, causing a momentary traffic snarl. I blew my whistle to move the traffic, and three birds lighted on me, two on my shoulder and one on my hat. I held up my sign that said STOP and waved the cars onward.

My first customer. He was as big as an ox and twice

71

as heavy. I blew my whistle and held up my sign and escorted said ox across the street.

"I didn't say you could go," I shrilled at a truck driver as I blew my whistle. "Get back here." I blew my whistle again. Horns sounded and tempers flared. "Just where do you think you're going?" I demanded. "You don't go till I blow my whistle. There are children crossing here. Now, move that truck and get back where you belong!"

"I can't back up. There's a mile of traffic behind me, and there's no room to pull over," the driver shouted.

"You're a troublemaker, that's what you are. Don't think you can practice your sign language on me. I went to Trail Guides, too. Now, you stay put! You're punished!"

"For what?"

"Because you didn't wait for me to blow my whistle. One more word out of you and I'll report you!"

"Report me to who?" the driver asked belligerently.

"It's for me to know and you to worry about whom I report you to. If you do that once more, I'm going to make you sit here all day. Shame on you!"

"Oh, yeah? You and who else?"

"I saw that! I saw that!" I yelled. "One inch closer and I would have gone up in flames! Get out of that truck right now and pick up that cigarette!" I blew the whistle in his cab. "Consider yourself reported," I said, scribbling his license number on the cuff of the suit.

"Look, lady, I have to deliver these tomatoes. I didn't know you couldn't throw a cigarette out the window," the driver said an hour later.

"I told you to be quiet. You're punished. Those tomatoes will be purée before you deliver them."

"How much money do you make?"

"Eight dollars a day," I sniffed.

"I'll give you ten if you let me go," he pleaded.

"Nope. Next time you'll have more respect for this orange suit."

Several days later my friend Pat told me she received a memo in the mail, saying the substitution of crossing guards was a thing of the past. She said there was also a vague reference to something about over-ripe tomatoes and stalled traffic.

Did You Say Physical Fitness?

When my ten-year-old son, David, came in from school and told me he needed an A in Social Studies (no longer relegated to history and geography) or he would have to go to summer school, I knew I was in trouble. In order for him to get the grade, I had to sign up for a physical fitness course, and I had to pass.

All the mothers (who but a mother would agree to such a dastardly thing?) were told to bring a bathing suit to the weighing-in-and-measuring ceremony, and the note said, Don't forget to bring your Project Leader (e.g., son/daughter).

Miss Winslow, who was a sizzling size three, told us to don our swimwear and let it all hang out. God, did it hang out! We were then measured and weighed. My Project Leader told me I was nine pounds overweight and had three inches too many, or a definite case of midriff bulge. Miss Winslow then spoke to each volunteer (I prefer the word "victim") and mapped out a program for us. Mine read:

Nine hundred-calorie diet.

Jog one mile each morning before breakfast.
Bicycle for three miles.
Fifty push-ups, fifty sit-ups.
Fifty windmills and fifty toe touches.
Note: Your Project Leader will observe your exercise routine and record your successes and failures. Your Project Leader will also supervise your meals.

"Now," Miss Winslow said sweetly, "I want to hear from each of you what your weaknesses are in regard to food." Silence. Project Leader Kuczkir said I ate four Twinkies a day.

"Traitor," I hissed.

"You are what you eat," he commented coldly.

Each victim had to sign in six different places agreeing not to cheat on the diet and, unless death overcame us, to stick to the exercise program. I signed my name and told my Project Leader I was going to string him up by the thumbs when I got him home.

The first day was a total disaster. I managed to jog the mile, but Mike had to come and drive me home. I swallowed my hard-boiled egg whole and did two sit-ups. I touched my toes four times and did five windmills. Push-ups were a fat zero. My Project Leader recorded my efforts and said I needed a jump rope with an odometer on one end and a speedometer on the other end. An hour before dinner I pedaled my three miles, and my husband had to pick up both me and the bike.

By the end of the fifth day I was weak from hunger and my skin itched. I also had dark circles under my eyes from lack of sleep. My Project Leader informed me I had to stop torturing myself by getting up to look in the refrigerator. Then David added, "If you hoot with the owls all night, you won't be able to soar with the eagles in the morning."

By the end of the third week I was up to nine sit-ups and twelve toe touches. I could do fifteen windmills, but push-ups were still zero. I could manage to jog and pedal and get home under my own power. I lost one and one half pounds. My three inches were still intact.

In a cold, unfeeling voice my Project Leader said he had no intention of going to summer school and something drastic had to be done.

"Listen, I don't have the strength to sign your report card. I don't care if you have to go to summer school or not."

"If I have to go to summer school, I can't go on vacation and I can't be on the swim team. If I don't go on vacation, neither do you."

"I know, let's kill Miss Winslow!" I cried feebly.

'Tis the Season to Be Jolly...

Last year, for the first time in twenty-five years of married life, I forgot the old adages "It's better to give than to receive" and "It is not the gift but the thought that counts."

Christmas isn't for kids, it's for mothers!

A mother joins a Christmas Club and makes the payments. A mother watches the circulars and ads and runs to the store so she'll be first in line when the store opens to get that special something there are only ten of.

A mother starts out with a list as long as Aunt Bluebell's paper towels, and it's a mother who stands in checkout lines for hours on end so she can carry home all the packages and lug them to the attic. It's a mother who later carts them down so she can spend endless hours wrapping them, and it's the same mother who totes them back up to the attic to store till Christmas Eve.

A mother is the one who knows exactly what will bring an ear-to-ear grin and a shine to a child's eyes on Christmas morning.

She's the one who helps Dad assemble the toys and bikes so he can play with them while she watches. And guess who it is who runs to the drugstore at ten minutes of six on Christmas Eve for extra tree lights and more batteries?

It's a mother who drives fifty miles to the farm for a fresh-cut tree. She's also the one who lugs it home so the house will smell like Christmas is supposed to.

Mothers decorate, trim the tree, bake, and cook for days on end for that special day.

For twenty-five years of loyal, devoted service, I figured this was the magic year when I would get something for myself; for me the person. I figured a quarter of a century should count for something.

From Cindy I received a chandelier for the dining room. Susy gave me a crock pot. Michael's contribution was a gift certificate for ten gallons of gas. Dave came through with an empty monogrammed bank. Patty gave me a wicker basket full of kitchen utensils. From the other half of this lasting relationship I got a one-piece bunny sleeper.

I thanked everyone for the gifts for the cook, the house, the chauffeur, and the financier, and where, I demanded, was the rabbit who was supposed to wear the bunny sleeper?

This year I decided to fix the lot of them. No more standing in lines, no more real Christmas tree, no more kitchen detail. No more exquisitely wrapped packages and no more trips to the attic. Good old Mom had had it!

I made up my list. For Cynthia, a health-food gift certificate. For Susy, newly married, a taste of her own medicine, an electric hamburger gadget. For Michael, who loves to be chauffeured, a sidecar for his bike so his friends can push him. For Patty, who doesn't know what patience is, a kit to hook rugs. For Dave, who loves to spend my money, a wallet. For the rabbit lover, a live one and a bag of pellets.

By the middle of November I started to feel like the Grinch and Scrooge, so I went out and did what I've done for twenty-five years. Everyone knows you can't teach an old dog new tricks.

Being a natural snoop (it goes with the profession), I decided to look around. In Cynthia's room, under her bed, was a cashmere sweater. For Mom, the card said. In Patty's room, under her knee socks, was a white box with a slender gold chain. The card said, Mom.

77

Under a pile of *Sports Illustrated* was a gift certificate in my name to a local bookstore. I was stunned; I didn't think Michael was aware that I knew how to read. I couldn't find anything in Dave's room. Susy doesn't live at home, so, all things considered, three out of five wasn't bad.

In my husband's dresser drawer with his one-of-a-kind socks was a jeweler's box with a charm bracelet. There was a single gold disc attached to one of the links. It read: "To the mother of my kids."

I always knew Christmas was for mothers; it just takes some people longer to find that out.

Take Me Out to the Ball Game

For any of you who don't know what a Little League Mother, a Little League Player, a Little League Coach is, I would like to share my personal views.

Would you, could you, believe that, combined, these people are the backbone of a future World Series? Believe it!

For the ten weeks of the Little League baseball season, the Little League mother is unique; she's one of a kind; she has no equal. She's the mother of that kid out there on the diamond playing his heart out for a team that is running a losing streak. The fast-food chains call her by name as she leaps through the door and grabs her order. She has no time to cook because she's either taking someone to practice or picking someone up. And if she's not doing that, she's watching a game and shouting herself hoarse.

Anyone who doesn't like hamburger, fish and chips,

or pizza is her enemy. She has to leave the house, lawn chair in hand, just as her husband walks in the door. He looks vaguely familiar; he must belong; why else would he be looking so longingly at the stove? You remind him in rapid-fire order that both kids have a game at the same time and you'll split the innings with him, and isn't it great that the fields are only three quarters of a mile apart? You remind him that it's Michael and the Dodgers that are having the losing streak, and Dave and the '76ers aren't doing much better. As you sail blithely through the door you again remind him the season only has eight more weeks to go.

Who but a Little League mother would alternately praise and boo the umpire and the coach, and not necessarily in that order? Who but a Little League mother would shout encouragement to a member of the opposite team when he makes a good play? Who but a Little League mother would give up a twenty dollar lobster dinner on Mother's Day to watch her son's ball game?

She's the one who sits through three innings of pouring rain, ruining a sixty dollar pair of suede gauchos and a seventeen dollar hairdo. She's the bleary-eyed, disgruntled soul who climbs out of a comfortable bed at seven A.M., dresses in a mix-and-match outfit (which later turns out to be all mix and no match), and drives four bright-eyed and bushy-tailed young players to the field.

She drives with one eye open, sipping coffee through a straw as she stops to pick up first one player, then another. Just when she thinks she can relax, one of these players takes a head count and decides someone is missing.

The Little League mother is the one who, with a muttered "go get 'em, tiger" collapses on her lawn chair, and it isn't until the second inning that she realizes she's been cheering the wrong team. She then looks around to see if anyone noticed and pretends her other kid is playing on the opposite side.

This unique, one-of-a-kind lady is the one who chews her seven dollar manicure down to the bare nub when her son slides into second base, tears his pants, and rips his knee open to the bone, an ear-to-ear grin splitting his face when the ump yells, "SAFE!" She doesn't worry that it will take seven stitches, a quart bottle of peroxide, a mile of bandage, sixty-four ounces of Tide, and a yard of thread to make it right. Instead, she forces herself to recall a promise she made at the beginning of the season not to leap the fence and "fuss" over him.

This lady sells raffle tickets, bakes cakes that other Little League mothers buy, and donates ten hours of her time to work in the stands selling candy, soda, and ice cream to the players. Win or lose, she's always there.

A Little League player is a kid somewhere between the ages of eight and twelve. He comes in assorted sizes and shapes and from every ethnic background. He's your kid; he's mine; he's everyone's son—or daughter.

During Little League season his marks in school go downhill. He can't divide twenty-two thousand eight hundred seventy-six by four hundred thirty-two, but he can rattle off the batting average for every player on the Reds and the Yankees. Math, English, and Remedial Reading will be there in September. Why bother with the trash? It will only fill up again tomorrow. Who can concentrate on mowing the lawn when the coach called for two hours of batting practice?

He's the kid who lives on shriveled-up hot dogs, petrified hamburgers, and pizza that defies description. He buys these nutritional gourmet delights at the field with the rest of his buddies. You watch in horror as he takes two bites and sticks the rest in his pocket to finish later, usually sometime between the fourth and fifth innings. You give him three vitamins a day and hope they work before rigor mortis sets in. He chews on an average of two pounds of bubble gum a week; no self-respecting Little League player would be caught without a wad of gum big enough to choke a horse. But you don't worry because half the coaches in Little League are dentists.

A Little League player's last words before going to bed at night, and his first words in the morning, are: "Don't forget to wash my uniform." He cheerfully decorates your bathroom with no less than six pairs of raunchy, smelly sweat socks that he "washed out" under the tap. You give the socks several quick squirts of Arpege and turn your eyes to a pair of mud-soaked cleats he left in the sink, along with a note bearing a happy face and a terse "Scrub these."

He's the kid who has to get to the field an hour early in case the coach has some miracle play that will help win the game. He mumbles and mutters, positive the coach was wrong and he should have bunted. When he gets to first base, his eyes apologize to the coach.

He's the kid who goes up to bat with the bases loaded and two outs and the other team—the one in the delicious red uniforms (your kids are plain blue) —leading in the next to last inning. He has a full count. His heart hammers in his chest as he swings the bat experimentally and takes a quick look at the coach. He swings and misses. The delicious red uniforms are delirious, but wait . . . those plain blue uniforms are all standing in the dugout, reaching out their hands to their friend and fellow player. You hear, if you're close enough, such comments as "Tough break"; "Good swing"; "We'll make it up in the next inning." And if you could see that far, and if your rose-colored glasses don't get fogged up, you would see that same ear-to-ear grin . . . Isn't that what it's all about?

A Little League coach is the guy who gives up his free time, his family dinner, his golf, and his bowling for ten weeks while he coaches fifteen young players.

He suffers untold agonies when his guys are out in the field or up at bat. He yells, shouts, and pounds the wall of the dugout, if there is one, until his hands are sore. His face, a mirror of his emotions, shows his grimaces and his delight as he mutters and gives pep talks with machine-gun rapidity. He speaks a verbal, as well as a sign, language that only his players understand. His praise is slow in coming, but it's sincere.

You'll never convince the Little League coach that he doesn't have a potential Pete Rose or Mickey Rivers on his team. This is a man who plays baseball in his sleep, a man who can rattle off the name of every kid on his team and then forget the name of his own.

I'm one of many Little League mothers. Those kids out there on the sandy mound and the carpet of green are our children. And those guys pacing the dugouts watching all the Pete Roses and the Mickey Rivers are the Little League coaches.

World Series Material? You better believe it!

The Aftermath of the Wedding

I like grandmothers. I like babies. I like grandmothers in general and I like other people's babies.

"What do you mean the frog died? The ink isn't dry on the checks I wrote to pay for your wedding. You can't be having a baby! If you have a baby, that makes me a grandmother. Why couldn't you use a rabbit like

everyone else? When you take a frog out of its natural environment, it's bound to die. Two frogs!

"I refuse to accept it," I said huffily as I stalked from the room. "I'm only forty-five, and that's too young to be a grandmother."

"Daddy thinks it's great," Susy said happily.

"Why shouldn't he think it's great? He has gray hair and a paunch. He looks the part," I sniffed.

"Grandmothers are sweet little old gray-haired ladies who sit on the front porch and rock in their rocking chairs while they sip lemonade. They smile a lot and have rosy cheeks. My God, I don't have a front porch. I get dizzy if I rock in a chair, and I would rather sit in some dimly lit supper club and sip a vodka gimlet. My red hair and rosy cheeks come from bottles. What kind of grandmother would I make? I'm not ready!

"Grandmothers buy the little kids balloons, and

then can't blow them up because their dentures get in the way. I don't even have a cap in my mouth," I dithered.

"It won't work. Grandmothers cook gorgeous turkey dinners with all the trimmings and make apple pies from trees in the back yard. We only have a forsythia bush. My culinary expertise is limited to tacos, spaghetti made with Ragu, and Lorna Doone cookies for dessert. Are you sure that frog died?

"I'll have to change my life-style. I won't be able to play tennis and I'll have to give up golf and water skiing. Whoever heard of a grandmother who goes cross-country skiing? I hate wraparound aprons. Henri Bendel will go bankrupt if I start wearing wraparound aprons.

"Grandmothers' houses always smell like home-baked bread and pine needles. Ours smells like smelly sneakers, and we have Stick Ups on the mantel to kill the odor. I'm not ready. I need at least twenty more years. Fifteen," I said fearfully. "So okay, ten, but that's my last offer. I'll go to the pet store and get a thoroughbred rabbit. Breeding always counts in the end. What did you expect from a frog out of a pond?"

The nightmare woke me and I leaped from bed, my eyes wild and my hair full of static electricity.

"Did the smoke alarm go off?" Mike grumbled.

"Worse."

"Did the dog throw up on the blanket?" he mumbled sleepily.

"Worse."

"Did the toilet overflow?" he asked, swinging his legs over the side of the bed.

"No, the toilet didn't overflow, and the reason I'm here talking to you while you complain about the damn toilet is, I had a nightmare. Listen," I said, grabbing him by the arm, "you have to listen to my nightmare. I was sitting in this . . . this . . . rocking chair. And a . . . baby . . . a real baby crawled over to me

84

and clutched at my wrinkly panty hose. That's how he knew who I was. Grandmothers always have wrinkly hose. Did you hear what I just said? He had a frog in his pocket," I jabbered as I downed a Seconal and three aspirins.

"Did you wake me up just to tell me about a dream with a frog? Go back to bed and stop making spaghetti with Ragu. It's the acid in the tomatoes that throws your system out of whack," my husband observed just before falling into a deep, untroubled sleep. The reason I knew it was untroubled was because I knocked him out with the lamp.

"We'll say it's adopted, and this way it can call me Mary. Adoption isn't the same thing as real. Of course, she won't be able to visit for the next six months."

My untroubled husband somehow managed to mutter that I would never get away with it since our daughter lived with us.

Fright or Flight

I called up my mother the other day (long distance, I want you to know) and asked her if she would like to take a trip to Guam to see Louise.

My mother, who is always one step ahead of me, asked, "Louise who?"

"Louise your daughter, that's who. Maybe we can talk Dory into going along with us. What do you think?"

"Think?" my mother said. "I never think when a

crazy daughter calls me up and asks me a crazy question."

"What's crazy? You said you only gave birth to one-of-a-kind-kids. Last week you said Dory was crazy."

"Okay, flaky," she said huffily.

"No, Ma, the week before Louise was flaky. I'm the normal one, remember? Do you want to go or not?"

"I'm afraid of heights, and there's too much water over the Atlantic. What if the plane goes down?" she questioned fearfully.

"Ma, we're going over the Pacific. This is your chance to prove what you've been telling me for forty years—if the plane goes down, that is."

"What's that?"

"That you can walk on water."

"Now I remember. You're the smart aleck."

"You got it. Are we going or not?"

"Some other time," she hedged.

"If I pay for the tickets, will you go? We'll stop in Hawaii and see Don Ho. He loves old ladies. We can surf and eat pineapples and do all kinds of good stuff, like hang out in bars all night and drink till the sun comes up. What do you say?"

"Guam is fifteen hours ahead of us," she said fretfully.

"Right, right. We'll arrive before we start and you won't lose any time. Boy, Ma, you really are clever. Does that mean you're going to go?"

"No, I'm afraid to fly."

"Look, Ma, we'll get snookered as soon as we get on the plane and you'll never know what it's all about. If the plane goes down, then you just get out and walk. Well?"

"What about your father, can he go?"

"Why not? But you'll have to hold him up; he's a mere mortal."

"He won't want to go. They show X-rated movies on those kinds of flights."

86

"Believe me, he'll go." I noted sagely.

"If the plane goes down, who will I leave my flight insurance to?"

"Leave it to Louise. You'll go happy knowing she's frittering it away."

"What if the pilot has a heart attack, or the plane gets hijacked?"

"Louise will think of something. A problem ceases to be a problem once you give it to Louise."

"Is she the flaky one?"

"Yeah, but she has smarts, Ma. She works for the government, so no one would dare hijack the plane. Are we going or not?"

"I'll have to go to confession, clean house, buy some clothes, and make a will. Did you say next year?"

"No, three weeks from now."

"But I just went to confession and I don't have to go for another month. I'll let you know."

"Ma, tell Dad the movie on the plane is *The Happy Hooker Goes to Washington.*"

"Smart Aleck," she said, hanging up on me.

Runaways

We all know what a runaway is, but did you ever have five kids depart the premises on the same day with a father for a chaperone?

Before the crowd departed, they called me such endearing names as dictator, female chauvinist, and a mother who is less than a mother.

I am the first to admit that I do not sparkle like the dew in the morning when I wake up.

Nor am I the sunshine in anyone's life until at least eleven-thirty in the morning. Monday through Friday, that is.

Saturday is a whole new ball game. On Saturdays I do not radiate at all. That's the day I turn into an unfeeling ogre.

When I entered the bathroom, I turned around and rousted every one of them from their cocoon of warmth and pointed to a pile of scattered underwear. In a voice that could be heard in the Big Apple, I threatened to hang each and every pair from the mailbox with its owner's name emblazoned in indelible ink for the whole neighborhood to see. That was the moment I became a mother who is less than a mother.

In my spit-and-polish kitchen that I had left the night before, rightfully assuming it would be that way in the morning, I found corn flakes, a trail of ants on my counter that looked like the New Jersey Turnpike, and a toaster hanging precariously by the wire. On the floor by the trash basket was a yogurt container that had missed, with a trail of wheat germ next to it. And there were three dirty, smelly sweat socks on top of the range hood. I just knew that the other one was somewhere at the end of the street. Mothers know things like that. When I threatened to move out, I became a female chauvinist.

"You're not wallpapering my kitchen today. You waited five years, so you can wait another week. Today is the day I have to make a dozen pies for the Little League bake sale." That was when I became a dictator.

After they left, I took my toothbrush and went to my mother's. She said I wasn't staying with her, because she had spent half her life cleaning up after me when I was a kid, and I could just go home and do my own thing.

Not This Mother!

Every child views motherhood in a different way. To my son Dave, who demands very little in life, she is someone who bakes raisin-filled cookies and makes his bed military style (a quarter will bounce off the covers).

Michael thinks this mother was put on earth to chauffeur him to and fro and is one who will sit through wind, rain, and snow to watch his athletic prowess. He's also the one who brings me flowers that he steals from the neighbors' gardens.

Patty views motherhood with a clear, sharp eye. To her a mother is someone who will shop endlessly and has a checkbook that never runs dry.

Cindy, who should know better, considers me second only to Dr. Spock.

Susy views me as someone who will listen to her rights and cause slogans. When I don't agree with them, she makes me a special sign to carry around that says I don't know where I'm coming from.

It took twenty-five years, but my husband finally said my stuffed cabbage was better than *his* mother's.

I don't know about the rest of the mothers of the world, but when it comes to gifts on Mother's Day, I get labors of love like jewelry containers made from cigar boxes and decorated with buttons sprayed gold, oranges with cloves stuck in them for my dresser drawers, homemade calendars in which every month looks the same, wilted marigolds in milk cartons, and flower arrangements made from Kleenex. And last, but certainly not least, "We're going to cook for you. You don't have to do a thing!"

They're right. It takes a cleaning crew of three to undo their good intentions.

What mother would trade all those labors of love? Not this mother!

5

The Head Honcho

It's All Over!

Taking five kids on an auto trip is bad enough, but if you add one father to the crowd, it's all over.

One would think, because he is a mature, responsible adult, he would understand things like pit stops every fifteen minutes, not to mention a little hand-to-hand combat in the back seat, and occasionally one needs nourishment.

It's comments like "You said it was only two hours by car, and already we've been on the road for five" that give mothers a bad name.

And let's not forget that detour signs and roads under construction apply only to dumb drivers, not the likes of him, and why didn't they put a sign a mile back on the road to warn motorists of the dead end?

Then there is, "But you said there was a gas station somewhere along here. The needle has been registering empty for ten minutes." Your reply that he said he'd be damned if he'd stop at that tacky-looking station falls on deaf ears.

When he wants to know why three of the children are sneezing, and you tell him it is because there is a dog and one hamster picking the feathers out of someone's pillow, he thinks you're talking to someone else and demands a coherent explanation or he's stopping this damn car right now and the rest of you can get out and walk, and all we need is your mother and next time we're getting a truck.

Why is it wives are permitted to take the wheel only

when it's pouring rain, rush-hour traffic, newly tarred roads, and interstate highways after midnight?

Instinctively, you know it's all over when a state trooper calls him Mario Andretti and tells him to pull over. Who does he blame? You got it! "My wife told me to step on it. She has a beauty parlor appointment in the next town."

Even behind the trooper's polished sunglasses I could see him eye my pixie cut, and I didn't miss the smirk when he wrote out a forty dollar ticket and told the driver to clean up his act.

Instant Invalid

Why is it when a husband gets sick it's *instant invalid?*

A wife can't get sick till she washes clothes, does the dishes, does the grocery shopping, and cooks dinner. God forbid anybody else in the family should know how to do these things. It also helps if she can put the kids to bed. A 104° fever is mandatory and a nervous collapse is a necessity. (On the part of the wife, that is.)

Periodically, my husband comes down with one of what I call his "mystery illnesses." You know the kind. "God, what can it be? Even my earlobes are hot to the touch." Or, "I'm dying, the hairs on my legs hurt." And then there is, "My hair follicles must be deformed, my head is killing me, and it's not a headache."

An instant invalid in our house demands the following:

A house call by a doctor who has M.D. after his

name. (It could just as easily mean "manic depressive.") I've yet to bet the rent on one of his clever diagnoses.

Gourmet meals. (He forces himself to eat things like *osso buco à la orange, roulade de veau florentina,* and why don't you whip up some cherries jubilee?) In between he mainlines double Oreo cookies.

Twenty-four-hour nursing care. Among other things, this includes someone who will fluff his pillows every fifteen minutes, someone who will work the remote control on the TV, someone who will turn the pages of his magazine, and someone who will run, not walk, with gay abandonment to do his bidding at every tinkle of his insidious little bell. This person must never gripe, complain, or show dissatisfaction as she goes about her errands of mercy.

When I get sick and take to my bed with some exotic illness like strep throat, the New Jersey flu, or a dislocated back, I receive the following:

Self-diagnosis, compliments of *What You Always Wanted to Know About Your Health, But Were Afraid to Ask.*

Campbell's soup that I heat myself on one of my trips to the bathroom.

Self-help. I don't have any pillows to fluff, because the person who shares the other half of my bed confiscated them, along with the TV, the magazines, and the bell, when he moved to the couch so he wouldn't "catch" whatever it is I *think* I have.

Isn't it wonderful what modern medicine can do?

The Bottom Line

"Look at this! Would you look at this!" my husband cried, pointing to a picture in the newspaper. "President Carter appointed a woman general to the Marine Corps."

"From the halls of Montezuma to the shores of Tripoli, those Marines?" I asked in awe, craning my neck to look at the object of his fury. "Yea, womanhood!" I chortled gleefully.

"Today the Marines, tomorrow the world! It's the end! No man's land will be just that, no man's land. I can see it now, field compasses by Cartier, designer field tents. Duffel bags by Louis Vuitton. Gucci combat boots. Crew cuts will be replaced with Sassoon hair styles. Blow dryers will be mandatory!"

"The Marine posters say, 'We're looking for a few good men.' So they found a few and now they want women. You're spinning your wheels over nothing. It doesn't say she's running the entire Corps. Information means questions and answers, that kind of thing."

"Nothing is sacred any more. Before you know it she'll outfit reconnaissance planes with Instamatic cameras. Folding chairs and sun umbrellas will be used for beach assaults. You'll probably be the first passenger to sign on when she turns the carrier *Nemitz* into another *Love Boat*," Mike said, banging his head on the wall.

"You're the one who voted for Carter. Take it up with him."

"If she buys M-Sixty tanks like you buy cars, they'll

be topped with vinyl roofs and have rich Corinthian leather on the inside. American Express cards will become standard Marine Corps issue. The men won't be able to leave their trenches without it. I bet her first order of the day will be to assign color-coordinated Princess walkie-talkies."

"You're not listening to me. It says Director of Information. That means questions and answers. Like the woman at Amtrak who answers questions."

"Sure," he snapped, "like, 'What time does the half-track leave for Jack LaLanne's?' Before you know it, the Joint Chiefs of Staff will be women. They'll sit in Schrafft's and argue over the tip. I'm telling you, it's the end! And another thing, wait till the next issue of the *Marine Corps Gazette* and *Leatherneck* come out. They'll be full of fashion news and gourmet recipes. That's it; I rest my case," Mike said furiously.

"It's about time. I keep telling you, it's questions and answers. You're getting bent out of shape over nothing."

"Okay, you say it's questions and answers. What if someone calls her up with a question about amphibious warfare? You don't think for one minute she's going to refer them to the Air Force, do you? She'll probably tell them to call back after she waters the plants."

"What plants?"

"The plants she's going to decorate with. And don't forget the curtains and the air fresheners."

"Do you think she'll order designer sheets and towels from Bill Blass?"

"Sure, sure, everything will be pastel. Everything will be peaceful and harmonious. Before you know it she'll replace the bulldog with a dove or a canary."

"That's it! Now I'm mad! You ready for the bottom line? There's one overriding, all-powerful force we women can yield, more feared by you men than the neutron bomb, and you aren't getting any tonight! Now, I rest my case!"

The Body, a Shrine?

Physical fitness programs are something I personally avoid, like trips to the dentist. The way I look at it, a woman gets a complete workout every time she goes to the supermarket. You really have to be a super athlete to avoid the rush down the yogurt aisle, and a long-distance runner to beat your neighbor to the express line.

One of our neighbors upset Mike recently by telling him that being fifty years old was over the hill. He suggested that Mike join him and three other "over-the-hill" friends for a trip to the local health-food store, where he promised my husband would again find his youth.

When Mike returned with a spring in his step, I looked at him with suspicion. "What is all this?" I asked as I poked in three of the super-looking black and gold shopping bags.

"Just a few things," he muttered.

"How much did these few things cost?"

"Eighty-seven dollars and ninety-two cents."

"Will all this stuff make you paint the living room, clean out the garage, give you enough energy to shovel snow, or retile the bathroom?"

"Not that stuff," he said, pointing to a bag full of vitamins. "Maybe the other bag," Mike offered, a sheepish look on his face.

"What is it?"

"An herb bath mixture."

I laughed when he said you had to add wheat-germ oil to the bath water so the herbs would mix well.

I rummaged in the bags some more and was amazed at the happy glow on my "over-the-hill" husband. "Does this mean I don't have to cook any more?"

"No, not at all. You take all of these before breakfast."

"You're kidding! You'll be so tired from bending your elbow you won't be able to go to work, and you aren't staying home with me. Two weeks of vacation and togetherness is all I can take of you," I said nastily.

"Look," Mike said, indicating the bottles. "Vitamin A for a peaches-and-cream complexion, and it will help me see in the dark. B-Twelve so I won't tingle in the extremities, C so I won't get scurvy and capillary hemorrhaging, D so rickets don't set in, and E," he leered, "for you-know-what! Magnesium for limber muscles, lecithin, kelp, and sea salt," he added, nodding toward the bag. "I need them for my twilight years," my husband commented piously.

"This is the pits!" I snapped as I leafed through an exercise book and tried to lift the weights.

"I have to start living again. I've been dormant too long," Mike cried dramatically.

"You're telling me!"

"When I'm hale and hearty, I'm taking off for wherever the trade winds blow."

"Be sure to tie the bottles of wheat germ to your ankles so the trade winds don't throw you off course!" I yelled to his retreating back.

The Vacation

Everyone knows, especially women, that men make the worst hospital patients.

When one of Mike's "mystery illnesses" came to fruition and the A.M.A. put a name to it, they admitted him to the hospital. Needless to say, he took a hairy fit over the whole thing. Talking about it was one thing, but living the experience was something else.

Every time I had to go to the hospital he would tell me it was a vacation, and then he would add insult to injury by saying I should enjoy my time away from home. When I told him the same thing, he was not amused.

"What do you mean this room is two hundred sixty dollars per day?" he bellowed to the admitting clerk. "I could take a trip to Aruba or spend three days at the Waldorf Astoria for less!"

Ensconced in his color-coordinated room, in a bed that did everything but play music, he almost drew blood when he found out he had to wear a paper gown temporarily. With very little effort he managed to rip five of them before he dived under his matching covers, yelling that his unmentionables were not for public viewing and just what the hell was he getting for two hundred sixty dollars.

A sweet young nurse, with the light of battle in her eye, told him he was getting three liquid meals a day at no extra charge, a box of his very own tissues, along with free towels and washcloths. She also said the doctor was going to throw in a free shave before surgery, and as an added extra bonus, the hospital itself was going to come through with a rubber tube for him to sit on, no strings attached. "If you get attached to it, you can take it home, but it will cost you ten dollars and ninety-five cents plus tax."

Aspirin, she mentioned, went for a buck a throw, and if he felt like that about the whole thing, he better not plan on getting a headache during his stay.

"You want me to do what in this bottle!" he yelled so loud he could be heard in the sunroom.

"You're taking more blood than I have!" Mike screamed an hour later.

"Don't worry, we'll give it all back later," the lab technician snarled.

"Just what the hell does that mean?" my husband hissed.

"It means they're going to transfuse you later, probably during the operation. Out with the old and in with the new, that kind of thing. You have to suffer when you come to a hospital. That's what it's all about. And we don't want to waste that two hundred sixty dollars, now, do we?"

"I don't like this place. I want to go home," he answered fretfully.

"Now, 'we' aren't going to make a scene, are 'we'?" the nurse cajoled, needle poised in midair. "If you do, then you get this right where it's softest, and 'we' don't want that, now, do 'we'?"

"Don't leave me," Mike cried anxiously as I made ready to go home.

"You be a good boy and just lie there and think about how miserable we're all going to be without you. If you're extra good, I'll bring you a coloring book tomorrow," I called from the hallway.

"I'd rather have a paint-by-number set," he yelled back.

Who's the Mother?

I turned the television on the other night in time to hear an announcer say, "It's ten o'clock. Do you know where your children are?" Every mother worth her salt knows where her kids are at ten o'clock. Patty is necking in the living room with her new boyfriend. Michael is punching out their brother in his bedroom, and Cynthia's gargling in the bathroom.

What the announcer should have said was, "It's ten o'clock. Do you know what your husband is doing?" Sure I know, the same thing he's been doing for the past twenty years, taking a nap before going to bed.

"I think you should sign up for one of those sleep courses. You can sleep your life away and get paid. Just tell them to mail me the check. If I tied a string around your neck, I'd have all slack. Don't you ever move?" I demanded, shaking him awake.

"Oh, God, oh, God," Mike yelled, leaping out of the chair. "I just had the most horrible, the most horrendous nightmare of all time. I was the father who had the baby in Joan Rivers' movie."

"That was a nightmare, all right. No self-respecting kid would want you for a mother," I said callously.

"It was terrible. People were congratulating me and booing me. God, it was awful. Billy Carter gave me a case of beer and said, 'Better you than me.' Henry Kissinger offered to take me for a spin to the Far East to show me off. Art Buchwald wanted to buy the exclusive rights to my delivery. President Carter said from now on it was onward and upward, and men and women were finally equal."

"But those were all men. What did the women say? Are they the ones who booed you?"

"You won't believe this, but Roberta wished me a case of terminal heartburn. Pat said she hoped I became addicted to water pills. Paula said she would pray that my swollen ankles hung out of my support hose. Joan said she hoped I had a Caesarean section and that the incision looked like the mark of Zorro. My very own sister wished me to have false labor every other night for the last two months of my pregnancy. And your friend Ann said she hoped the doctor used heavy-duty twine for my stitches."

"Poor baby," I crooned.

"Don't say that word. Don't ever say that word to me again."

"Why wasn't I in your dream?"

"I don't know. What would you have wished me?" he asked, dozing off.

"The only thing that's left. An eleven-pound, four-ounce breach birth."

The Big Day

In our house Father's Day is the day of days, second only to Christmas.

Most fathers are called by many names: Dad, Daddy, Pop, Father, and, by some, the Old Man.

In our house he has other names: mechanic, electrician, plumber, part-time tutor, and father confessor.

A father can be counted on to do and say many

things, like, "Either you turn off that garbage or the stereo goes." Mike can be witty and charming when he says, "He who does not work does not eat."

He has no equal when he screens boyfriends with the eye of an eagle, and he's an expert at saying no before the question is asked. He's also the guy who foots the bills. (We hear that a lot.)

I've personally seen Mike develop terminal deafness on more than one occasion, especially when one of the kids had the audacity to ask for an advance on his allowance.

Our father is the person who said the miniskirt was a fad and no daughter of his was wearing one. (Once in a while he goofs.) And he still cringes when he sees them in a bikini, but he never makes the same mistake twice.

You know he's a great guy when he can still smile and look enthusiastic as he receives his eighty-fifth orange can covered with felt paper and adorned with silver macaroni, or his thirty-fifth cuff-link box made from popsicle sticks.

And on Father's Day, when we offer to take Mike to the eatery of his choice, where does he decide to go? You can count on him to opt for the golden arch and a Big Mac, even though he knows he'll get instant heartburn.

Would we change him?

No way! It took us twenty-five years to train him this way.

6

It's a Woman's World

It's My Inalienable Right!

A woman who prefers to remain nameless at this writing said to me recently that she starts off each day by exercising her inalienable right to bitch, grumble, gripe and complain.

Immediately, I identified with her, since I start my own day in a like manner. I never thought of it as something due me, it was just something I did automatically.

"Did you know that mothers are the most powerful people in the world?" she asked. "Everyone in the entire universe has or had a mother. We wouldn't be standing here if we didn't have a mother."

"What about fathers?" I asked curiously.

"Come on! Did you ever hear of a father who had a baby?"

"Well, not actually having a child, but without a father you don't have a ball game."

"Think about it for a minute. Mothers outnumber motherless women ten to one."

"That's a pretty impressive comparison. Are you sure it's accurate?"

"No, I'm not, but I like the way it sounds. Mothers control this country to a certain degree, and given half a chance, we could dominate the entire thing. Right now we have the strongest influencing power over the cereal companies. Take a good, long look at the appliance industry and tell me we didn't make it what it is today. And who does Detroit have to thank for their color schemes? People like us. Mothers."

"How about just women in general?"

"You're weird," she said, fixing her steely gaze on me. "If you replaced Sadat and Begin with two mothers, there would be no more Middle East conflict. Mothers can solve everything and anything."

"Except the problem of whose turn it is to do the dishes."

"If mothers ran this country, we wouldn't have things like political winds, breakdowns in communications, or open confrontations. Peace, that's what we'd have. No more premature withdrawals and no more reciprocity."

"Wait a minute. Are you saying that if mothers ran everything, there would always be open negotiations and the world would be in a constant state of detente?"

"Exactly. A mother is the most powerful woman in the world."

"If a father or a man gets wind of some of your ideas, there will be a primal scream that will be heard around the world," I whispered.

"Your father already tried that, and he's been sent to his room," the nameless woman said.

It Might Be a Man's World, but I'm Paying Cash!

The day my '67 Mercury Comet gave out I made the decision to buy a new car. I also made the decision to purchase it on my own.

"You're nuts!" Mike said succinctly. "What do you know about engines and tires and the inner workings of a car? Women can't buy cars!"

"That's what you think. I've been liberated and I can do anything I want. Besides, who cares about the engine? I'm only interested in the interior, the color, and the stereo system."

"Oh, my God!"

My first three stops were a fiasco. My husband was right. The salesman wouldn't wait on me, probably assuming I was looking and not buying, and that I would have to come back with my husband.

It just so happened, when I made my fourth stop, a sale was in progress. To my practiced eye there were six salesmen and three prospective buyers on the floor, which should have qualified me for some exclusive attention.

Once I found the car of my dreams, I tried to get a salesman's attention. They all ignored me. Having no other choice, I did what any woman would have done. I hopped on the hood and yelled, "I'm paying cash!"

After I revived them with an ammonia ampoule that I'd discovered in the glove compartment, told my six personal salesmen that I wanted the car I had been standing on. Following the ensuing fight, I sat in my new car with the stick shift that I didn't know how to operate and marveled at the rear defogger, the elaborate stereo and tape deck, not to mention the crushed-leather bucket seats and an instrument panel equal to that of a 747.

"And it has steel-belted radials," I told my husband happily.

"Just what you need, steel-belted radials to go to the supermarket," he observed not too happily.

"I got three sets of keys and a can of paint in case my orange stripe wears off."

"But you don't know how to drive a four-speed shift," Mike complained.

"What's to learn? I'll practice in the driveway."

"You're reasonably intelligent," my husband said, "so just give me one good reason why you bought a sports car with four on the floor. Is silver and black with an orange stripe just one good reason?"

108

"Is that what's bothering you? The salesman said I looked ten years younger behind the wheel. I'm not stupid, you know."

Mike understood my reasoning, but he told me that only after I had revived him with the smelling salts that came with the car.

The Give-Away that Got Away

"You're sixty dollars overdrawn on your checking account, and the battery in the car, your car, is shot," my husband said coldly. "You've been sitting in the car playing the radio again, haven't you?"

"Where else can I go when your mother comes?" I asked defensively.

"Don't bring my mother into it. This time you're going to have to make good. Get a job," Mike said smugly. "If you don't, then I'm going to cut off your lifeline."

"My credit cards," I bleated.

"And the telephone," he added ominously. "You'll be cut off from the outside world!"

"A job! Me!" I was properly horrified after I had recovered from the shock. "If I get a job, who is going to cook, clean, sew, and work her fingers to the bone?"

"The same person who's been doing it for the last twenty years, the cleaning woman."

"I don't know how to do anything," I whimpered.

"This is true," my husband agreed. "You'll think of something."

109

Two hours later I found it in the Help Wanted section. The perfect job for someone like me.

>Ladies! Ladies! Ladies!
>No experience necessary! On-the-job training.
>Car helpful.
>An equal opportunity employer.

I pursed my mouth as if I had swallowed two ounces of vinegar. Actually, I told myself, the ad

didn't have to mean "that." I would wear Mike's wet suit with snorkel attached when I applied.

"I'm here," I trilled as I made my way into the warehouse to meet my new employer.

He certainly was impressive, all nine feet of him, I thought as I clutched the zipper of the wet suit.

"I don't know if you're exactly what we had in mind," he said suspiciously as he eyed the wet suit.

"I was scuba diving," I informed him coldly.

"There's no water for thirty miles," he replied just as coldly.

"We have this creek . . ."

"Okay, okay. As long as you're here, let's talk."

"The ad said: Lady. I am a lady," I said, throwing out my thirty-two triple-A chest. I quickly followed up with, "No experience necessary. I have a car, see?" I pointed to my '67 Mercury Comet with the bucket seats. "I qualify!" I claimed triumphantly.

He grimaced. "One out of three ain't bad."

"You're tormenting me, aren't you? You probably wanted voluptuous redheads," I said petulantly as I replaced the snorkel.

"Naw, I like wet suits," he snarled. "Okay, now listen to me. This is a give-away program. We're giving out free samples of beltless maxi-pads. That's a sanitary napkin. What you have to do is give a free sample to every apartment or house that is listed on this map," he informed me pointing to a tiny square of paper.

"Is that all? Anyone can do that," I said breezily.

"That's what the last wet-suit applicant said."

"Oh, yeah? What happened to her?" I asked suspiciously.

He shrugged. "That was ten years ago. I've never heard from her since. You'll have a thousand boxes to distribute. The pay is one hundred dollars. Do you think you can handle it?"

"Of course," I snorted indignantly.

111

He looked pointedly at my feet. "Those fins are going to slow you down a little," he said snidely.

Two days later, promptly at the noon hour, my give-aways arrived. God, did they arrive. The driver of the tractor-trailer that was parked in my driveway announced in a voice that could be heard all over the neighborhood, "I got your thousand boxes of beltless maxi-pads with the self-stick strip."

The following day at sundown my neighbors, who were having a barbecue and block party in the middle of the road, gave him a twenty-one gun salute as he pulled out of my driveway. The ambulance and police car that were standing by turned on their sirens as he roared down the road. "The plastic bags are coming on another truck," the driver yelled over the noise.

"What did he say?" my husband demanded as he tried to peer over the boxes that were heaped everywhere.

"There's been a mistake. The man said a thousand boxes. He gave me too many. He gave me a thousand cartons with forty-eight boxes in a carton," I cried pitifully.

"I won't be able to see if the fog comes in tonight," Mike complained. "I can't even see the house across the street."

"So what? You don't like the looks of their house, anyway," I snapped as I leaped over a carton. "Oh, my God, what if it rains!"

A set of thirty dollar shock absorbers, forty-five dollars worth of gas, seven hundred boxes still to go, and sixteen days later, I called up the man at the warehouse and quit the job.

"I told you those fins were going to slow you down. If you quit now, you have to pay me three hundred dollars for the undelivered give-aways. Read the fine print. Give-aways are not returnable."

"What?" I screeched.

"Either pay up or go to jail."

"Mike, listen to me. I swear I'll never sit in the car and play the radio when your mother comes. I'll use the calculator when I balance the checkbook. You heard me the first time. Three hundred dollars or I go to jail. Mike!" I screamed. "Answer me," I cried, juggling the button on the phone. "Are you there? Why aren't you answering me?"

We insulated the attic.

We insulated the garage.

We insulated the toolshed.

The Ten-Day Magic Diet

With summer fast approaching, the girls at the afternoon bridge club decided it was time they did something about their weight if they wanted to wear something besides their Omar tentmaker dresses.

Paula, who resembled an Oreo, said she had a diet that made all other diets obsolete. "This diet," she vowed, waving a paper in the air, "is foolproof and guaranteed. Or we get our money back. So far, nobody has asked for a refund," she said, reading various testimonials from participants of the plan. We oohed and aahed when she claimed we would all lose five pounds a night while we slept.

"What is it?" I asked, my previous experience at Ye Olde Fat Farm still vivid in my mind.

"It's predigested protein."

"Who digested it first?"

Paula scanned the fine print. "It doesn't say. It just says take two tablespoons a day."

"What do we have to do?" Joan asked.

"It's what we all have to do," Paula answered. "First of all, I made arrangements with Marge Simmons to feed the kids three times a day. Our husbands can either eat in the city or starve. We're going to clean out our refrigerators and cabinets and keep only cottage cheese, lettuce, and Jello in the house. We're going to police each other." Paula then made us all sign our names in blood, and we went home to think about what we had committed ourselves to.

Part of the master plan was that we would let our exhaust fans run day and night, so that any cooking aromas would waft down the street. Joan said it was to be the honor system all the way around, and anyone caught cheating would be ousted from the afternoon bridge club. Since this was a fate worse than death, we all agreed that we would sort of hide out and keep in daily telephone contact. We were to meet on the tenth day and have our unveiling on the island at the end of the street.

I was the first to arrive, but only because my kids gave me a ride in their Magic Flyer wagon. Carol came by skateboard, holding on to her daughter for dear life. Paula rolled down the street and got stuck in a firethorn bush. The kids had to pull her out and drag her the rest of the way. Ann stuck her head out of her dining-room window and said she could hear everything but she couldn't make it. I sent the kids to give her a ride in their wagon. It took Joan a little longer than the rest of us because she kept falling off her son's tricycle. When her son seated her for the third time, I knew she would make it.

By twelve o'clock we were all present and accounted for.

Joan tried to open her book to record our weight loss but had to give it up as a bad job. We were all wearing our Omar tent dresses since none of us had any energy to pull up a zipper on something else.

"What went wrong?" Ann cried pitifully.

"I'll tell you what went wrong," I gasped, trying

114

to get to my feet. "That magic diet of Paula's didn't say we would be making twenty-three trips to the bathroom every night. That's how you lose the weight. For God's sake, didn't you read the instructions?"

"Paula never reads instructions till she breaks something," Joan muttered. "I knew we never should have trusted her."

Grumble, Grumble

At yoga class the other day, I listened to several of my friends complain about their lives. Joan was upset because her daughter had mono and chicken pox, Cris was turning into a whiner, her husband was staying out late, and on top of that her very own mother was coming for an extended visit. "Plus," she said ominously, "there's this guy who has been turning around in my driveway three times a day."

Paula said she could do better than Joan's list. She said Jessie and Rachel decided thay wanted new glasses, so they gave their old lenses a workout with her skin machine. Max wasn't coming through with the alimony and child support. The dog bit the kid next door. In addition, she was being sued by her best friend. Furthermore, her radar range ceased to function and her sewer was backed up all the way to the street. "And the same guy who's turning around in Joan's driveway is turning around in mine."

Pat griped that Stan was into beer and pretzels and refused to cook dinner any more. Her crab apple tree got split down the middle by a Sears Roebuck truck, and all they said was, "Sorry, lady." Her cat Whiskey had just delivered a litter. "It was the first virgin birth in my house. What the hell am I going to do with nine kittens?"

"Such petty complaints," I muttered. "If you want real problems, just watch the soaps. Now, *they* have troubles. Why, do you know that Brad can't function without Jenny, so he confessed to Rita, who's a hooker, that he hates kids but loves sex? And then," I whispered, "Marco learned that Becky is using the name of a retired singer, and who do you think is Lianview's Becky Lee? And now we all know that the dresses and makeup Vinnie had been hiding from Wanda were used in his decoy-female vice squad."

"Yeah, I really feel sorry for Wanda," Joan said sadly. "I guess I can put up with chicken pox and my whiny kids."

"Does anyone know who's suffering on The Y & R?" Paula asked.

"Oh, sure," I volunteered. "Lance and Leslie swore to cherish their few special moments together, and then got mad at Laurie for her lack of sympathy for Les. Brock pleaded with a snookered Kay to give Derek his walking papers. Brad is soothing Chris, whose nerves are frazzled because of Karen's fate. Liz quit her job and Kay got mad because she's seeking revenge on Jill. Chris had second thoughts, gave up Karen to the Beckers, who split, and then she took a walk to sort of think things out."

"I wonder what Liz would have done if a Sears Roebuck truck had split her crab apple tree down the middle?" Pat asked.

"Maybe we should send that into the program. It's time some of those actors found out what real-life drama at home is like," Joan said.

The Sexy Age

Why is it when you're on the sunny side of forty (that's anywhere between thirty-five and forty-four), all the birthday cards are about sex? Last year, when I was still in the sun, I received these thoughtful suggestions:

Have a real sexy birthday. Well, at your age, do the best you can.

You're at that awkward age, somewhere between tri-weekly and try weakly.

Birthdays are just like sex maniacs. They're on top of you before you know it.

Stay away from sex on your birthday. You'll need all your strength to blow out the candles.

For a happier birthday remember Ben Franklin's words: "Sex beats flying a kite in a storm."

Last week, when I crept into the shade (that's anywhere between forty-five and ninety-nine plus), all the cards I received had subtle messages about my age:

You're not over the hill—just down the road apiece.

Hope you live to a ripe old age. Another year should do it.

Remember, the best years are yet to come. That's called positive thinking.

Don't worry about your age. Just decide what it is and stick with it.

You know you're getting older when your get-up-and-go sits down and says, "The hell with it."

You're at that exciting age—somewhere between anything goes and it got up and went.

You're not getting older; lots of people wear corrective blue jeans and orthopedic sneakers (this one was sent by my better half).

I did get two straight cards. The first one read: We can take pride in the fact that our family tree has, for generations, produced serious, responsible citizens! Then there's our branch.

The second card read: It's good to know there are still people like you in the world . . . bitching, complaining, and griping like the rest of us.

I also got a Barrel Of Fun Activity Book. The instructions on the front of the barrel said if you colored in the lines, you could peel a star off the back and paste it at the top of each page.

Life Begins at Forty

My friend Joan called the other night and began to babble incoherently as soon as I got on the phone. "What's wrong, did someone die? Did your husband cut off your credit cards?" I asked anxiously.

"Worse! From now on it's all downhill! The end is in sight! I can see it all now," she cried dramatically. (She does everything dramatically.) "First the wrinkles will show, then my hair will fall out, Jack will ask for a divorce, and the kids will want to start with those *informal* marriages. It's all over!"

"There's nothing worse than having your credit cards cut off," I said in a voice that rang with experience. "What's over? Who's going downhill? Oh, my God, I'll be right over."

She was right. What could be worse than the trauma of hitting forty?

A bottle of tequila and all the accouterments in hand, I raced next door and clasped my friend to my bosom, all the while mouthing soothing words of comfort. "Look, either you're going to accept this disaster or you're going to fight it."

"I'd rather die than fight. I'm too tired and too old. It's the end," she cried pitifully. (When she isn't being dramatic, she's being pitiful.)

"There're two ways you can fly on this," I said, chock-full of authority. "If you're going to pack it in, then you tuck in your wings and buy a rocking chair. The next step is to demand a nest egg in your own name. RCA and General Motors will do nicely. You can count your dividends while you rock in your new chair. This is the perfect chance for you to let your hair grow back to its natural color; you always said you wanted to see what the 'real you' looked like. Besides, whoever heard of a good-looking chick in a rocking chair? This is your chance to look as tacky as you want. Now, in my opinion, that's downhill!"

"See! See!" she cried hysterically. (When she isn't being dramatic and pitiful, she's being hysterical.) "It's the end—there's nothing to live for!"

"It doesn't have to be that way. You do have another choice. You can spread your wings and fly. This is your chance to start a whole new life. The first thing you have to do is begin comparing yourself to beef. Forty is prime. Anything else is chuck or ground round. For starters, make a sizable withdrawal from your joint account. Get a new hairdo and some new clothes to go with your new image. Buy a sports car. Every forty-year-old woman needs a sports car to cruise around in. If that doesn't take a big enough chunk—you've earned it, he's had the best twenty years of your life—consider a face lift or a breast

119

transplant, or live dangerously and slice a few inches off your hips. Join a card-carrying women's lib group. When you're tooling around in your fancy sports car, you can cut down every male chauvinist who crosses your path. Forget about your trick knee and take up cross-country skiing. You can try to seduce your husband—I said try—and when he says, 'Not tonight, dear, my back aches,' you can take a page from his book and say in a voice that drips venom, 'I was just testing you, I'm not really interested.' You can run away from home a couple of times a week. Holiday Inns love forty-year-old ladies."

Six Tequila Sunrises later, my friend Joan asked if there were any other options open to her. I decided to give her the benefit of my wisdom. (Later I realized it wasn't really wisdom, but five Tequila Sunrises too many.)

"What the hell, do what every other red-blooded American woman does. Lie! I've been thirty-nine for the past six years. I look at it this way: when I apply for Social Security, I'll be the youngest one in line."

My friend Joan said she would drink to that.

The Sensuous Age

"This coffee klatch is going to be a bust," Joan observed. "There isn't anyone left to pick apart, and there's no news in the neighborhood."

"Why don't we just drink our coffee and talk about the weather?" I suggested.

"I have a better idea. Let's take this sensuality test

120

that I clipped out of a magazine. I'll ask you the questions and you give me your answers."

"How come I'm always the guinea pig?"

"Because I'm the one with the test. Ready?"

"On a scale of one to five, how do you rate your sensuality?"

"I thought at our age it was called tired blood. How about a one?"

"Are you imaginative in the bedroom?"

"After you hit forty, imagination is all that's left. I'll give it a one. How am I doing, Joan?"

She ignored me. "What's your feeling on meaningful relationships?"

"Does that mean with or without a husband in residence?"

Joan said the test didn't specify with or without.

"I suppose if he didn't bring his dirty laundry and minded his own business, I'd give it a two."

"How often do you take a sexy bath?"

"The last time I took a bath, sexy or otherwise, was when I hurt my tail bone and had to soak for an hour every day. I take showers. One."

"Have you considered wearing a bikini to tantalize your husband?"

"Oh, sure, I considered it, but they only give you two pieces of cloth when you buy a bikini. How would I cover the leftover cellulite? If they came six to a suit, I would buy one."

"Is your voice husky and sensual?"

"When I scream and yell all day, I have a husky contralto. Does that count?"

Joan said she didn't think so.

"Do you think other men find you attractive?" she continued.

"With five kids and tired blood, what do you think?"

"For every old shoe there's an old sock. It's women like you who give the rest of us a bad name. What

121

you need are massive doses of vitamin E . . . on the hour," Joan said, closing the magazine.

"Where are you going?" I demanded. "It's your turn to take the test."

"Are you kidding! I could never top your answers. I'm going home to order some vitamin E."

7

Slavery is Passé

The Dream Machine

We have machines that take men to the moon and machines that take men to the bottom of the ocean. And now, according to an article in the paper, there is a machine in some bars and taverns in which a person can insert a coin in order to take a test that will give a reading on the level of alcohol in your system. After giving the percentage, the display board will flash one of three messages: "Don't drive!" "Take it easy!" or "You're O.K.!"

If they can come up with a machine for drunks and would-be drunks, why can't they come up with one for the poor beleaguered housewife?

Wouldn't it be great if we could wake up in the morning and plug in to see how we should spend the day?

Question: Should I wash the windows?

Answer: No way. It can be hazardous to your health.

Question: Should I paint the den today?

Answer: Absolutely not. Hire someone.

Question: Do you think I should scrub the kitchen floor this morning?

Answer: And get housewives' knee? Forget it!

Question: What's your feeling on bed-making?

Answer: Negative. You're just going to mess it up tonight.

Question: Is today a good day for doing laundry?

Answer: No day is good for doing laundry.

Question: Should I cook dinner today, and if so, what should I cook?

Answer: Only chefs cook. Have you heard about the fast-food chains?

Question: What should I do today?

Answer: A little R & R would be nice, if you toss in some music and a Harvey Wallbanger.

The Husbandly Challenge

We went to a party the other night where the after-dinner entertainment was provided by the husbands.

The entertainment (I use the word loosely) consisted of all the husbands (mine was the ringleader) saying housewives did nothing all day but push buttons, attend kaffeeklatsches, and read romances.

The end of the lively discussion that followed was that Mike was going to make up a list of things to do the following day. He bet his Telly Savalas autograph against my copy of *What You Always Wanted to Know About Sex but Were Afraid to Ask* that I couldn't do his few simple errands and still take care of the house and cook dinner.

Cheered on by my peers, I accepted his challenge, but only because I didn't want him to get his hands on my book.

The following morning I made breakfast at six o'clock, packed lunches, and drove the kids to three different schools and Mike to the train station. When I got home I loaded the dishwasher and pressed button number one. Then I stripped and made two sets of bunk beds and pushed button number two on the washing machine. From there, I vacuumed and dusted. When I finished I made a pot of spaghetti sauce, and while it cooked I cleaned off both patios and carried the lawn furniture into the garage for the winter. I pushed button number three to dry the laundry, and let the dog out and in again. At eleven-thirty I sat down to eat breakfast, lunch, or brunch, or whatever.

I pulled out my husband's list, which any good, qualified pharmacist would have been glad to fill.

Fill up gas tank, buy pastrami, get twelve one-inch screws, take shirts to Chinese laundry, pick up new television antenna, and why don't you make something good for dinner for a change? P.S. If you hop to it, you can make it home in time to read a whole book.

There was no signature.

It was five minutes past twelve when I pulled into the gas station. Nothing happened. Aha, self-service! I prayed nobody was smoking as I watched the line form.

The next stop was the deli and pastrami. After I crawled over twenty cases of antifreeze and fought my way through a pack of Cub Scouts loading up for a field trip, I tripped over a floor-waxing machine that seemed to be operating by itself. The deli owner cut my pastrami, strapped up both my ankles, and helped me to my car. He told me not to hurry back. He should worry; with the prices he charges, he'll never see me again.

Screws. At the hardware store I couldn't see the cash register, let alone the one-inch screws, for the mountains of fertilizer and peat moss. I finally managed to work my way to the back of the shop where I thought the screws would be. Wrong. Coffeepots, ironing boards, and bayberry candles filled the aisles. I whistled between my teeth like the kids do, and two cats poked their heads out of the coffeepots and looked at me. I tried it again and one of the cats knocked over the ironing boards. I hated to be a quitter, but there was no way I was going to buy screws from a cat.

I had to stop the car once on the way to the Chinese laundry to let out one of the cats that had come along for the ride. It was two-thirty when I carried in the soiled shirts and handed them to a young man decked out in a business suit that had a button saying he was a Harvard man. He wouldn't take Mike's shirts. He said they only sold Farrah posters now, and how many did I want? I took three along with my dirty shirts and went back to the car.

My last stop was for the television antenna. I listened while the salesman conned me into a super-deluxe job that cost one hundred twenty-five dollars and would, he said, bring in Aruba and the Virgin Islands. "For that price I should get Hawaii and Don Ho," I snarled.

It was four-forty when I walked into the house after picking up the kids. I wasted another half hour arguing with the paperboy who wanted me to take a second subscription to the paper because that way he could win a skateboard. Dave took the subscription, and if the kid wins, he gets the skateboard on alternate Saturdays.

Along about this time the dog wandered in, smelling suspiciously as if she had made contact with the sewer at the end of the street. One bubble bath and one bottle of My Sin later, I looked at the clock and saw that it was a quarter to six.

With fifteen minutes to kill, I had to make a decision: hang up the Farrah posters or cook dinner.

I'll admit to one thing. Farrah looked a lot better than my spaghetti tasted.

Over My Dead Body!

One of the first things you learn when you move to suburbia is that you never sign your name to anything, and only over your dead body do you allow an appliance to be removed.

128

"How could you let him take the television?" my husband bellowed. "How can I watch the Mets to-night?"

"You told me to get it fixed or you weren't coming home this evening. Listen to the game on the radio or go next door and watch it."

"If I go next door the entire neighborhood will know you let the set out of the house. Why didn't you just give him Sam?"

"There wasn't anything wrong with her. He said

he had to have the proper tools, which are in his shop. He also said it was a two-day job."

"Why does this slip say we signed up for cable TV?"

"We aren't getting cable TV."

"Oh, yes, we are, and we're getting a new antenna. Your signature is clear as a bell. The least you could have done was scrawl it like doctors do. That way we would have a fighting chance. When and if that set gets back here, we won't recognize it."

"He said he had seven kids, two dogs, and three cats. Someone with a brood that size to take care of wouldn't do anything dishonest," I said, remembering his shady eyes.

"How do you think he supports those seven kids, two dogs, and three cats? Get that set back right now, and I'll repair it myself," Mike thundered.

"He's closed at night. Why don't you stand outside the Knights' window and watch the game? They'll never know you're there."

When the shop opened the following morning, I was the first customer. "Look," I said, working my way around the seven kids who were helping, "I have to take the set. My mother-in-law is coming, and she needs it to watch the soap operas. I have to have it," I said firmly as I screwed the bulbs into the set.

"I just started to work on it, and believe me, it's one sad case. I got it just in time," he informed me as one of the three cats crawled inside and started chewing the wires.

"I'm sorry, but my husband broke his leg last night and he needs something to watch," I snapped, pushing two of the kids out of the way as one of the dogs nipped at my heels. "I don't want cable TV and my antenna is just fine. Shame on you, you tricked me. I'm paying you for the service call and that's all."

"You can't do that," he said, fishing a bone out of the back. "You see, this could be part of your problem."

130

"Just pack that television up. I'm taking it home."

"By tomorrow this set will be in apple-pie order," he continued, sticking his head inside. One of the kids, who was sucking on a slurpee, tripped when his older brother pushed him, and the icy mush splashed all over the interior of the television. When the man temporarily withdrew his head, the front of his hair was singed. He said he would have to charge me extra for medical treatment.

I ignored his screams of outrage as I pushed him inside the television and screwed the back on the set. Some way or other, one of the seven kids, two dogs, and three cats would free him.

I stopped by Appliance Arama and bought a boob tube and had it installed within the hour.

Mike noted I had probably set some sort of precedent, since nobody ever got their television back from a repairman. "Yes, sir, he must be a prince among princes. He even sanded and polished it. All the scratches are gone and it works better than before."

Total Disaster

The moment I finished reading *The Total Woman,* which a harried librarian had mistakenly checked out with my other books, I rushed to the phone and called my mother. "I'm crushed, I'm devastated," I babbled. "According to this book, I'm not a total woman."

My mother, who can be a bit feisty, replied that when I left her room and board twenty-five years ago, I was normal in every respect, and if something

131

happened in the interim, she wasn't taking the rap.

I hastened to explain that a total woman was the ultimate in women, and on a scale of one to ten I registered minus zero.

My mother asked how old I was and told me not to believe everything I read.

"I'm forty-five and holding," I snarled. "Why shouldn't I believe everything I read? You do. Who bought a copy of *The Hite Report* and then ran out and bought a shower massage?"

"I read the book, but it was your father who bought the shower massage, to take a shower," she said huffily. "You said your marriage was made in heaven and that you were happy."

"Ma, that was twenty-five years ago. What did you expect me to say on the second day of my honeymoon? I feel ethereal from time to time," I added defensively. "According to this book, I'll never be happy until I become a total woman."

My mother told me to stop whining and get to the point.

"The book says I should call Mike at work and tell him I crave his body and that I hold it in reverence."

My mother said I was nuts for reading such a book and offered to loan me her copy of *The Hite Report*.

I ignored her and continued to jabber. "It says I should dress up in outlandish costumes to greet my husband at the door at night. A good example is pink baby-doll pajamas and white boots. The book says if I do that, he'll chase me around the dining-room table and all the kids will giggle. You still there, Ma?"

My mother told me to stay put. She was coming right over with *The Hite Report*.

I figured I had a little time before her arrival, so I rushed across the street to my friend's house, the book clutched in my hand.

"Don't do it," Joan laughed.

"Well, I was sort of thinking . . . What I mean is, I've always wanted to be one of those exciting women

132

. . . you know, the kind who make men drool and salivate at the mouth. The last time Mike did that was when I made a pot roast and added apple juice to the gravy. I've always wanted a big bosom and long legs, and what did I get? I'll tell you what I got. I got a husband with a Good Conduct medal, five kids, a dog and a virgin hamster named Frizbee who gave miraculous birth to fourteen little Frizbees, and four goldfish who live in a zip-lock bag. If I become a total woman, maybe I can make up for the long legs and big bosom."

"Forget it. I already tried that bit and it didn't work," Joan gurgled. "Remember the time Jack locked himself in the car for three days? I dressed up like a bunny, and he's never been the same since."

"That was a cute idea. Didn't he like fuzzy rabbits?"

"What's to like? All I wore was the tail. From that day on, all his mother wanted to do was discuss the breeding habits of rabbits. I don't let her in any more."

"I can top that. Right now my mother is on the way with a book that is supposed to have the *real* answers, *The Hite Report.*"

"Do yourself a favor, trade books with her. There's a lot to be said for shower massages."

There's also a lot to be said for my mother's arrivals. She climbed from her 1962 VW, dressed in the latest Calvin Klein outfit, with a copy of *The Hite Report* in her hand for all the neighbors to see.

After Mom convinced herself I wasn't going through the change of life, and after she gave me a thirty-minute dissertation on stupidity, she went home with *The Total Woman.*

Two days later I called her. "That's it, you finished the book? Is that all you're going to say?"

"My dear, I'm seventy years old and more of a femme fatale than that author will ever be. If you want to make an ass of yourself, be my guest."

133

"But, Ma, I have to be typical and predictable, otherwise my husband won't love me," I wailed.

My mother said she hadn't given birth to any typical, predictable children, that she had created only one of a kind. She said if I washed my face with Dove soap and then patted on Oil of Olay for my complexion and brushed my teeth with Closeup for a whiter, brighter smile and took a dip in a pond and washed my hair with Earth Born shampoo, Mike would think I was beautiful. She said she saw all that on television, and they can't lie on television like some people who write books that she would rather not mention.

"I'm going to try it for a while. Maybe I can write an article on my experiences and sell it to some magazine."

My mother said the *Atlantic Monthly* didn't buy that kind of article.

We made a five-dollar bet that I would or would not succeed, and I retired to the den to map out my lesson plan.

Several days later I called her again and read my list of things to do. "Don't say anything, Ma, just let me read it through to the end."

1. Never nag. Never try to change Mike. If I don't nag him, he'll give me money and will do anything I want as long as I do exactly what he says, when he says it.

2. I have to lust after him. If I do that, his cup of emotion will run over, and, Ma, guess who gets to bask in the overflow? The one who fills the cup, me.

3. I have to love his body because he loves his body. If I pay him one good compliment a day, he'll blossom before my eyes.

4. Listen to this one, Ma. The book says only his ego counts, but this is not to be considered a slave-master relationship. Actually, what it means is a total woman graciously consents to adapt to her husband's ways, even though she might detest the idea. If I do this, he will shower me with goodies. It's kind of like

a royal affair; he's the king and I'm the queen. As the queen, I get to express my feelings, in a royal way, of course. The book says the king relies heavily on the queen's opinions, but he still makes all the decisions. The king doesn't want a queen with dignity, opinions, and spunk, but one who will give up her mind to him.

5. Once a week I have to call him at work and tell him I desire his body.

6. I have to meet him at the door every night for a week dressed in provocative costumes.

7. I'm supposed to prepare myself for a sexual on-slaught seven nights a week.

"That's it, Ma; now you can say something."

My father came on the phone, demanding to know what I had said to make my mother faint. I read my father the list and he hung up on me.

At ten o'clock the following morning I called Mike with his first compliment. "I like the way you comb your hair," I blurted.

"You'll do anything to aggravate me, won't you? If you don't like the way I comb my hair, why don't you just say so? Oh, no, you have to make a snide remark about how I'm going bald."

Undaunted, I continued. "I think you look great in your Quiana shirt. You should buy at least a dozen more just like it."

"If you'd iron it, I'd look a lot better."

Instead of giving myself a gold star, I marked a red minus on my list. There are those among us who just can't accept compliments, I told myself.

Day number two. Dress up in some outlandish costume. Since I just finished some sweet savagery called *Captive Passions,* in which the heroine was a lady pirate, I opted for a pirate costume. I slipped on a pair of short shorts, tied a see-through nylon blouse into a knot under my bosom, and donned my eldest daughter's knee-high black boots. Something was missing. I high-tailed it to the garage, ripped off a red rag that was nailed to a stack of two-by-fours, and paid my

135

daughter's room another visit where I confiscated her Cher wig. All I needed was a cutlass and I would be ready.

I hacked off the broom handle and Scotch-taped the carving knife to the end. If I didn't try to castrate anyone, it would hold.

Promptly at six P.M. I stationed myself at the door and waited for Mike. When I heard his car in the driveway, I gave my cutlass a few swipes in the air and stood back, feet slightly parted, like the heroine

in the book, and a wicked gleam in my eye. The moment the door opened I brought up my cutlass and yelled, *"En garde!"*

My poor bedazzled husband turned tail and ran across the street, crying, "Get the net!" to a neighbor who was digging out dandelions from his front yard.

I called my mother and told her what happened. She said Dad would deliver the net and not to go away.

Onward and upward to my next assignment. Call your husband and tell him you want his body.

I started dialing Mike's number fifteen minutes before he was due to go to lunch. Busy. When I finally got through, his deep voice said hello.

"Hi," I drawled in what I hoped was a sensuous voice. "How about coming home and we'll make wild passionate love?"

My sophisticated, debonair husband demanded, "Who is this?"

"I'm the lady pirate who almost cut you down last night," I snarled.

My husband told me to lay off the vitamin E and said he had a meeting scheduled for one o'clock and he was sorry he couldn't oblige me.

"Okay, how about a rendezvous in the Sears Roebuck parking lot and some quick fooling around?"

Mike agreed, saying he could pick up the new catalog at the same time.

Our neighbor almost fell off his sit-down lawn mower when I exited the house in my backless, semifrontless dress with the slits up both sides.

When I climbed into my husband's car and smiled sexily at him, he looked pointedly at his watch and said, "You have exactly eleven and a half minutes to get on with your epidermal stimulation, and then I have to get back to the office." He also told me not to get out of the car or I would be locked up for indecent exposure. He advised me to think on the matter while he went inside Sears for the catalog.

I took the catalog and went home and called my

137

mother. She said there wasn't a hole in the net, and how did I get loose?

Around this time Mike started looking at me as if I were a fly on sticky paper. On the fifth day he presented the perfect test. He said he had a four-day weekend coming up and we should go away. He thought I looked like I needed a rest.

Aha, I thought, the queen gets to voice her opinion. "Why don't we visit my sister in Ohio?"

The king, who relies heavily on the queen's opinion, said he was aghast that I would come up with such an idea. He said my dippy sister was as dippy as my mother.

"Then let's go to Swacker's Pond and fish. We'll tie the poles to a tree, and while the fish bite we'll have an orgy."

My husband told me everyone does that and we just did it two weeks ago. "We'll go to New York and see some baseball."

"You know I don't like the Yankees," I complained.

The king declared we were going, and that was the beginning and the end.

I ran upstairs and called my mother. I'll give her one thing, she is smart, at times.

"He read the book. Why else would he be playing the part of the king?"

8

He Who Sticks Together Will Not Become Unglued

Disco Fever

The newest craze to hit the land, as everyone knows, is disco dancing. If there's one thing I love to do (besides spending money), it's to try new things, to the acute discomfort of my husband.

When one of my precocious neighbors said she knew someone who would give the couples in the neighborhood disco lessons, I was for it one hundred percent.

When I broached Mike (fearfully, I admit), he singed my tail feathers immediately.

"Do I have to remind you that I am fifty years old?" he yelled irritably.

"God, no! Why can't you think of fifty as a number instead of as half a lifetime?"

"Because the last time I did that you got me into yoga, and it took a chiropractor, a podiatrist, and the Rescue Squad to untangle me!"

"Are you going to let one bad experience ruin your life?"

"Yep."

"You need the exercise," I said, eyeing his midriff. "Just think, you'll be able to turn, twist, and stretch your body in ways Fred and Ginger only dreamed of doing."

"Nope."

"Disco dancing is sharp, fast, and sensuous. I'm the first to admit you're no John Travolta, but maybe you could work on a fast shuffle. I'll pretend you're with someone else."

"Nope."

142

"In time you'll be as light-footed as Astaire, and if you concentrate you might get some of John's flexibility. All you need is a little work . . . from the neck down."

"Nope."

"Can't you think of it as a giant step forward for mankind? You get to wear a black and white outfit. Tight pants and a shirt open to the waist. We'll dye the hair on your chest; too much gray."

"Nope."

Every good woman has an ace, and I played mine.

"Guess who the teacher is. Martina Williams, the one who looks like Dolly Parton."

"What kind of dye will you use on my hair? Do I get to wear a gold chain around my neck?"

I didn't think there was any reason to tell him Martina filled in for her husband only when he was overbooked.

Why Don't "We" Plant a Garden?

My husband, horticulturist that he is, decided "we" should plant a garden. He informed me I could can and freeze the summer crop, then we would feast on it all winter when the snows and blizzards came.

I told Mike I wouldn't even consider it unless I had a Gucci sunhat and Gucci gardening gloves.

My next request was for a rototiller, shovel, and spade. My husband implied heavily that only inexperienced gardeners needed those kinds of things.

Dressed in my Gucci sunhat and Gucci gardening

gloves, I shrugged and attacked the ground with my eighteen-inch wooden spoon.

"When you're finished, give the spoon to the boys so they can start on the root cellar," Mike called from his position in the hammock.

"Will it have a door?" I asked craftily.

"Of course it will. Root cellars always have doors."

I made a mental note for myself to be sure I was wearing my Gucci sunhat and my Gucci gardening gloves when they thawed out his body in the spring.

"This ground is like clay," I called out as I brushed a crow off my hat.

"You just don't want to do it. You don't care if we starve next winter. Admit it," he sniped.

He had a point. The part about my not wanting to do it.

"I think you're supposed to mix something with the soil," I said.

"I know that," my husband answered petulantly.

"Every gardener knows you're supposed to mix coffee grounds, orange peels, and potato skins."

"We drink instant coffee, oranges give you hives, and everyone is on a diet, so we don't have any potato skins. This red clay is blinding me. I need a pair of Gucci sunglasses with my initials."

"Improvise. The answer is no."

"What are we planting?" I demanded arrogantly. It's easy to be arrogant when you're wearing a Gucci sunhat, Gucci gardening gloves, and Gucci sunglasses with your initials.

"Strawberries, asparagus, and artichokes. Why don't we try peanuts?" my husband suggested sleepily from the hammock.

"Why not indeed?" I replied, dusting off my Gucci gloves. "Is this what we'll be feasting on all winter when the snows and blizzards come?" I yelled. Then I remembered where he would be wintering. "Never mind," I added happily.

I dumped in five pounds of bran that Dr. Ruben said would save my life, a box of salt, and a carton of flavored bread crumbs. It didn't look like much, so I added a box of Fruit Loops and twenty-three Lipton tea bags. While Sam mixed it up, I practiced looking out of my monogrammed sunglasses.

When I told Mike I was taking our one and only stalk of asparagus to be preserved in plastic, he actually snarled at me and said the reason the garden didn't come up was because I couldn't see what I was doing, thanks to the initials on my Gucci glasses.

Free Advertising

Mike zeroed in on me the other morning when he saw me getting dressed to go out for the day. Right here and now I want to say the dreamboat of my dreams sprang a leak.

"Just give me one good reason why you have to decorate yourself with emblems and initials every time you go out. You're an honest-to-God walking advertisement. You cost me a bundle whenever you leave the house."

"Don't you want me to be in style? Do you want people to say I look tacky? I have to wear these clothes so everyone will know I'm paying three times what they're worth. Your problem is, you're not into couture."

"If you play your cards right, you could make money renting out your body space. I think it's time I got a return on my investment. Think about it. We could rent you out and make a fortune every time you walk down the street," he said, already scribbling on a piece of paper.

"Is this going to be one of those lectures on spending money?" I asked huffily.

"On Monday morning you could rent your neck and feet out to Anne Klein. In the afternoon you could parade around with your Gucci belts and Mark Cross handbags. Double rental!

"On Tuesday you could lease your chest to Dior and Givenchy.

"Wednesday would be good for your rump and Calvin Klein's bluejeans.

"Thursday could be set aside for Halston and his perfume, and you could probably work in Von Furstenberg and her sunglasses. If you really want to clean up, you could make a deal on the side with a Rolex watch.

"Friday could be special. You could wear one of everything and really rake it in. With your smarts, you can figure out a way to have Yves, Cardin, and Pucci panting after you. In a few weeks you should be able to name your own price. We'll be millionaires!" Mike exulted breathlessly.

"My mother always said you were a smart aleck," I sniffed. "Tell me who shops at Brooks Brothers, tell me whose emblem is the golden fleece, and tell me who spends too much every time he walks in that store!"

What Did You Do to It?

Why is it when an appliance breaks down, the first thing a husband says is, "What did you do to it?"

And when the repairman comes, after the switchboard operator has stated, "The service call is nineteen dollars and ninety-five cents. Do you still want him to come?" he says, "What did 'we' do this time?"

"I didn't do anything and 'we' didn't do anything. The damn thing broke all by itself without any aiding or abetting from me."

"We've been married for twenty-five years and you're on your ninth toaster, fourth washer and dryer, third refrigerator, and second dishwasher. Your track record leaves a lot to be desired," Mike muttered as he saw another twenty bucks going down the old drain. "When I tell the guys at work that you keep the Roto-Rooter man on a yearly retainer, they laugh at me."

"You forgot to mention that I'm on my fourth electric fry pan. If you didn't blab my business around the office, nobody would make fun of you."

"Their wives have the same appliances they started out with," he continued to mumble.

"That's because they weren't making them back in in the eighteen hundreds. I know a lie when I hear one. Don't think I'm allowing myself to get dishpan hands. Either have it fixed or I'm going on strike!"

"If you want that dishwasher repaired, you'll have to get a job to pay for it. Nine to five for a few weeks won't kill you."

"Nine to five! That sounds like a prison sentence!"

"Even you wouldn't have the nerve to tell the repairman David tied his sneakers to the silverware rack and ran it through the sanitary cycle! Would you!"

"I don't have to tell him anything as long as I have nineteen dollars and ninety-five cents plus cash for parts and labor. Let him earn his money."

"That's what you said when the last guy came to fix the dryer. If you don't tell them what's wrong with it, how can they correct it? It's like going to a doctor and letting him guess what's wrong with you. You cannot dry peacock feathers in a dryer!"

"You were the one who told Michael to help me clean house. Is it my fault he ran the hose over the feathers? Do you have any idea what wet peacock feathers smell like? If you won't give me the money, I'll do it myself!"

"How?"

"The same way I mend everything around here. With bubble gum, bobby pins, and Krazy glue."

That was three months ago, and aside from the fact

that once in a while, especially on the rinse cycle, we get a few bubbles that ooze out the door, the machine is working fine.

So Starve Already!

When "Sweet Savagery" found its way to supurbia, the women took to it like ducks to water, but not so the husbands. They fought it every step of the way and then some. A case in point.

"Do you think," my husband demanded, "that you could take your nose out of that book long enough to cook dinner?"

"Now? You want me to cook dinner now when Dominic Challenger is going to brand the inside of the heroine's leg? I wouldn't cook now if you told me President Carter was coming to dinner!"

"How long is it going to take Dominic to brand her thigh?" Mike asked, a look of disgust on his face.

"God, at least seven pages; otherwise I'm going to ask for a refund."

My husband was incredulous. "Seven pages to brand a thigh," he said, leaning over my shoulder, "and the type is small. I could do it in one line."

"Look, you don't just brand someone's thigh, you have to work up to it gradually."

"Will you make dinner after that's done?"

"Depends on how much she's suffering. I have to identify with her. That's what 'Sweet Savagery' is all about."

"Pages. Give me pages. How many pages is she going to suffer?"

"Probably a whole chapter. She'll have to have a trauma or two, and then she'll have to weep and wail and bemoan her plight. I wish you had a little romance in you," I uttered as I went back to the action.

"You wouldn't believe how hard it is to be romantic when you're starving," Mike said pitifully.

"So go to McDonald's and give the kids a ride home."

"If I go to McDonald's, will you promise to cook a roast tomorrow?"

"I can't promise. Joan is giving me her copy of *Delta Blood,* and I promised to give it to Paula at six o'clock. You can go to the Pizza Hut tomorrow. You haven't been there this week. I have to see how the author makes a macho hero out of a man with one arm and one leg."

He wouldn't give up. "How about Wednesday?"

"Sorry, Roberta is bringing over her copy of *Captive Passions.* It's all about a lady pirate who castrates men. There's even a diagram."

"Oh, my God!" my husband cried, collapsing on the couch. "When are you going to make the beds?"

"Probably on Thursday, after I ˙read *Madelaina.* She's raped by all of Pancho Villa's army, and after she gets away she falls into the clutches of Zapata's men, and they rape her, too. Then one month later she makes love with a man who tells her she smells like a flower. And do you know, she never had a bath in all that time! Marvelous, isn't it?"

"Does that mean you aren't doing the laundry? If you know the story, why do you have to read it?"

"I keep telling you, I have to suffer and identify, otherwise there's no point in reading these things. Besides, I'm addicted to them. I'm free Friday afternoon between three and four, unless Paula brings over her copy of *Valentina.* Now, there's a good one. That book has two macho heroes, and one of them has a black panther. They fight over Valentina, who gets raped, is

150

sold at an auction, and then ends up running some old guy's harem. God, I can't wait to read it!"

"If you get *Valentina,* that means I have to go to Arthur Treacher's. Aren't you ever going to cook again?" he cried passionately.

"Are you kidding! After I read all these books I'm going to write a sex manual for our neighbors."

"How about a cookbook instead?" Mike pleaded as he shuffled out the door.

Profit Versus Loss

When my husband pulled out the profit-and-loss sheet he keeps on me, I protested vehemently, for all the good it did.

"You have to stop this reckless spending," Mike commanded imperiously.

"I haven't done a reckless thing in my entire life except marry you," I grumbled.

"It's time to tighten our belts. You're spending more than I bring home."

"I never go anywhere, so how can I spend money? Obviously there is a mistake on your P and L sheet."

"Listen, anyone who buys vegetables from the Jolly Green Giant, dinner rolls from a Poppin' Fresh Dough Boy, cookies from the Keebler Elf, corn flakes from Tony the Tiger, and tuna from a mermaid is doing something wrong."

"You're absolutely right; we should stop eating. You have my vote. I hate to cook."

"And while we're on the subject, how do you justify

151

buying traveler's checks from Karl Malden? We didn't go anywhere to warrant buying traveler's checks."

"I like his rosy nose and I didn't want him to lose his job. Someone has to buy them. I used them in the supermarket."

"That's a stupid reason," my husband snapped.

"Just about as stupid as your buying a Mercury Cougar because Farrah Fawcett advertised it. And who was it who got bent out of shape when he found out she didn't come with the car? I rest my case," I sniffed.

"So all right, we'll go over the P and L sheet another time. But you aren't off the hook, just remember that."

"Sure I am. I don't have to cook any more."

Split with a Kit

My husband, who is one of your more basic male chauvinists, recently canceled our subscription to the daily paper when he read how a self-enterprising woman started a business called Divorce Without a Lawyer.

In his tirade against free enterprise he was quick to point out that this same woman also peddled Self-Bankruptcy Kits for seventy-five dollars, Legal Separation Kits for thirty-five dollars, and Make Your Own Will for seven dollars plus tax.

According to Mike, for ninety-nine dollars and fifty cents plus tax, the *Split With a Kit* divorce guide contained all the necessary forms and information to win an uncontested divorce.

I rapidly scanned the article. "Look, it says they

give out bumper stickers. For free! I want one for my car!"

"I want to know the name of the dumb cluck who let her get away with something so stupid," he said, jumping up and down in agitation.

"The dumb cluck was the New Jersey Supreme Court!"

"Well, no one will ever buy them," he snorted indignantly.

"Wrong. The paper said she sold six hundred of them. Get it through your head—women are here to stay!"

"This world is going to hell," Mike mumbled. "First we get Bella what's her-name in New York with her crazy hats, and if that isn't bad enough, we now have women generals in the military. And let's not forget you're the ones who started this whole sexual revolution!"

"Yeah, it's a shame you didn't want to participate," I sniffed.

"Before you know it, women will be running the world!" he cried wretchedly. "You're into everything but funerals. It's a damn wonder she doesn't have a kit on how to bury the dead. Gotcha! There are no women morticians!"

"Believe me when I tell you it was no oversight on her part. If she's half as smart as I think she is, she probably figures women did their bit by bringing you into this world and it's up to you men to usher them out!"

Did You Say Size Five?

If there's one thing that will strike fear into the heart of a wife, it's an invitation to her husband's twenty-fifth-year college reunion. Up to now I had always been pregnant and managed to avoid these momentous occasions when they came up.

Out came the yearbook and there she was. Jodi Masters. "A perfect size five," my husband said, a wicked gleam in his eye.

"No one in this whole world is a perfect size five except a midget."

Mike smirked. "She was voted the one most likely to succeed."

"At what?"

"At what? At what?" he mimed. "At everything. She had it. Boy, did she ever."

"Harumph! I bet she's married to a truck driver and has nine kids and is as broad as you are."

"Never!" he yelled in outrage. "Not Jodi!"

"Who's the super jock?" I asked, pointing a finger at a delicious-looking football player.

"Harumph! That's Cal Williams. All surface, no depth. All brawn and no brains. Not even enough sense to come in out of the rain."

"Well, he can eat crackers in my bed anytime," I said loftily.

"Just like a woman—judge a book by its cover."

"What we have here is a double standard. What makes the jock different from the midget?"

"I'm not even going to answer that," Mike bristled.

154

We attended the reunion with another couple, college friends of my husband's.

The reception committee handed out cardboard numbers that each graduate was to wear around his neck, and a Xerox list with each person's name and number.

"You realize that they darkened this room on purpose, don't you?" I said to Dottie. "Who do they think they're fooling? Look at all the paunches. If we draped a sheet over the lot of them, they could pose for the Goodyear Blimp.

"Look, Dottie, number twenty-three is Alice Rowe. Didn't you tell me she and your husband were a steady twosome? Would you look at her!"

"How many pounds would you say she's hiding beneath that muumuu?" Dottie sniffed.

"God, at least two hundred. She's supposed to lead a cheer. I hope she can lift her ankle."

"Ceil Winters is standing by the punch bowl. Get a load of those glasses she has on."

"She looks the same as she does in the yearbook. Mike said she was very studious and afraid of boys."

"Afraid of boys, huh? She married Cal Williams."

I always did hate crackers. "She probably seduced him by discussing the quantum theory.

"Look at number one. That's Jodi. What color would you say her hair is?"

"Purple, orangy-purple."

"No, she's standing under the colored lights. Looks more like winter white. Maybe ecru. I hate ecru. And look at the wrinkles. The size, what size is she?" I demanded.

"If you want a snap answer, I'd say she was three quarters of a doorway with a quarter of Paul Vincent."

"I went through six hours of wasted adrenalin before I got here," I complained to Dottie. "We're the only ones that got better, not older, and we didn't even graduate with the class."

Dottie grinned. "Do you suppose it's because we're five years younger?"

I'm Not Selling!

"I want to know what these bills are," my husband yelled as he waved a batch of papers under my nose. "Ever since you bought that stupid car I've had nothing but bills, and you haven't even taken it out of the driveway. What's this charge from Charlie Citgo for fifty-six dollars and twenty-five cents and this note attached that says eight dollars miscellaneous?"

"You have to pay extra when you have gas delivered," I snapped.

"But you never took the car out of the driveway," he snapped back.

"It's all that stopping and starting that does it," I said virtuously.

"Okay, I'll give you that one, but what's this bill for eighty dollars from a chiropractor?"

"Every time I shift into second I get whiplash. Do you want me to go into traction?"

"No, just sell the damn car!" he bellowed.

"Never. That car is me."

"You've had that car for seven weeks and it hasn't moved from the driveway."

"My leg is too short for the clutch. I need a block on it like you used to put on the kids' tricycles."

Mike ignored me. "Why don't you take a ride to Roberta's and let her see your car?"

"Don't be silly. If I go to Roberta's house, I'll *have* to go into traction. I would have to downshift nine times, and that would undo all the good the chiropractor has done."

"Go to Pat's."

"There are two hills on the way to her house. I'll slide backward and someone might damage my spoiler."

"What about the shopping center?"

"Are you out of your mind? And have someone rip off my tape deck and steel-belted radials? I'll never leave my car in a public lot!"

"In your opinion, when do you think you'll be ready to take the car out on the road?" my husband asked curiously.

"Maybe by Thanksgiving. It's too soon to tell."

"But this is May. What are you going to do between now and Thanksgiving?"

"Look, I'm not stupid, you know. I haven't even started to practice in the rain. That's going to take at least two months."

"That takes you to July. What are you going to do then?"

"I'm going to my mother's for the whole summer. I won't have time to practice."

"That brings us to September."

"Do you think I'm going to take that beautiful car

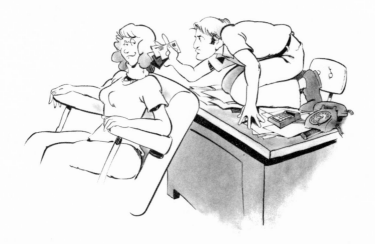

out on the road with all those school buses? Never!"

"What about October?"

"And have every kid in town see my new car? October is Halloween. Just forget it!"

"Thanksgiving?"

"You got it! By then I should be ready. The day I see the kids stop blessing themselves is the day I'll take the car out on the road."

"I know someone who will take that car off your hands, no questions asked. You might even make a profit."

"I'm not selling. Who? How much of a profit?"

"Me. Fifty bucks."

"You must be out of your mind! If I sold you my car, you would take it out on the road and every cop in town would be on your tail. They just wait for cars like mine so they can give out tickets. They work on a quota system. No way. I'm not selling."

Winner Take All

Can a woman with a sinus condition find happiness in a gambling casino?

I think it's safe to say my husband bounced off the wall when I suggested we venture to Atlantic City to try our wings.

Actually, what Mike said was, every man has his price, and, by God, he was going to find out what mine was before I put him in the poor house.

Then he said if we went to Atlantic City I wouldn't even get a chance to try my wings, because they would be clipped as soon as I entered the casino.

"Look," I cajoled, "think of the plane fare we'll save by not going to Las Vegas. By driving to Atlantic City we'll save five hundred dollars, and I know you wouldn't like Las Vegas, it's too noisy. You'll love the showgirls, the good food, the terrific decor, and the boardwalk in Atlantic City."

"I know you," he snapped. "Theoretically, it is impossible to beat the house at blackjack by memorizing all the cards in the deck. Your sinuses will bother you; the casinos are too close to the ocean."

"I'll suffer! I'll suffer! I'll just play the slot machines and forget about blackjack."

"That's what you said in Aruba. You can't play the slot machines; you have arthritis in your shoulder."

"I'll force myself to ignore the pain every time I pull the lever," I protested.

"Gambling is the same thing as throwing away your money," you-know-who said virtuously.

"I'm saving us five hundred dollars by not going to Las Vegas. If I save it I should be able to spend it!"

"You can't charge chips at a casino, and you know

you aren't happy unless you're charging. Don't you know any other word but 'charge'?"

"Sure. How about 'check'? Gambling casinos take checks. I watch television, so you can't buffalo me."

"We're not going, and that's final!"

"Okay, okay, but I want my money."

"What money?"

"My five hundred dollars that I saved by not going to Las Vegas."

You Have to Talk to Communicate

A news commentator announced in an ominous voice the other evening that if married couples would turn off their television sets for one hour each night and talk to each other, their marriages would have a better chance of surviving.

"Oh, my God," I dithered. "Turn it off. I'm too old to support myself and five kids. Hurry up, we have to synchronize our watches and start talking."

"You're nuts," my husband said. "If I turn off the television, I'm going to miss *Little House on the Prairie*. Stop believing everything you hear."

Silence is not golden.

"Well, say something," I yelled.

"I'm missing *Little House on the Prairie* and I'm mad."

I ignored his outburst. "What did you do today?"

"I worked my fingers to the bone like I do every day."

"Well, that's a start. What are you going to do tomorrow?"

"Nothing. I won't be able to do anything because my ears will hurt from listening to you talk, and I'll be aggravated and nervous because I missed *Little House on the Prairie* and won't have anything to talk about at lunch with the guys."

"You need help," I said smugly. "How would you like me to recite *Chicken Little* for you? It might take your mind off this conversation. In case you aren't getting the message, we are not communicating."

"Write me a note. Now can I turn on the television?"

"No, and if you try I'll break your arm. We're going to talk if it kills you."

"Okay." Mike gave in agreeably. "How much money did you spend today? Or should I say, how much did you charge?"

"None of your business. I said let's talk about normal everyday things."

"That is normal. Every day you spend money and and every day you put me one step closer to the poorhouse."

"There's no such thing as a poorhouse," I said loftily.

"Okay, debtor's prison."

"They only have debtors' prisons in England. Let's talk about going to Hawaii on vacation."

"Why don't we talk about how you scorched the chicken tonight?"

"Watch it. Burned chicken tonight. Tomorrow, no food at all. Let's talk about going to Puerto Rico if you don't want to go to Hawaii."

"I have a better idea. Why don't we talk about how I'm going to cut off your credit cards, including the beauty shop? *Now* can I turn on the television?"

There's a lot to be said for communication.

9

A Mixed Bag

A Rose by Any Other Name

I've seen expectant mothers spend the entire nine months of their pregnancy searching for the perfect name for what they hope will be the perfect baby.

The day the new mother signs the birth certificate, she is entirely convinced\ her perfect child will go through life bearing his perfect name.

What she doesn't know is that as soon as the kid hits his first playground or his first day in school, some dastardly little fiend will hang a handle on him and he'll be stuck with the nickname for the rest of his life.

I have a friend who is tall, svelte, and absolutely gorgeous. She said she was called Goober when she was a kid, and she threatened to kill me if I ever told her husband.

A neighbor whose name is Matthew is called Chew, another answers to Fig, while still another will turn if you address him as Woodie.

A psychiatrist, who lives two doors away, smiles when you call him Inky because of his fondness for giving the Rorschach test.

I come from a small town with a population of eight hundred or so, depending on new arrivals and who is being ushered out, where everyone knows everyone else and nicknames are a standard staple.

I went to school with kids who were called things like Blubber, Cob, Mouse, Diz, and Squeaky, and with a little bit of a thing called Dolly. Even the principal had a nickname. We called him Boomer because a day didn't go by without his lowering the boom on someone.

I was not exempt. My parents were not one of those couples who pondered and searched for the perfect name. Mom remembers that Dad took one look at me and said, "She's such a dinky little thing, do you think she'll make it?"

The day Boomer gave out the diplomas, he called, "Mary Ruth," and no one moved. Then he said, "Come and get it, Dink."

I'm forty-five and I still answer to that ridiculous name.

The Real Me

Because I'm a writer, people often ask me what kind of person I am. The first time it happened I said, "I'm just like you, except I'm a writer." I know what I'm like, but how do you explain yourself to someone else?

When people kept on asking me, I did what any other writer would have done. I got a book called *Astro Analysis Sun Sings Compatibility Guide* to see what I was like. And do you know something? It had my character down to a science, and it knew more about me than I did. Somehow, in the back of my mind I can't get rid of the idea that my mother had something to do with it.

The book stated I am an Aries, which is the first and most refreshing sign of the whole zodiac, represented by the ram.

The first chapter explained it is my nature to rush in,

to burst upon the scene as brisk and as vibrant as the season that marks my birth, which is spring. I am rash, full of life, impulsive, and spontaneous. I am always where the action is, but seldom there when it's over and time to clean up.

A few paragraphs later, it said I want the world and I want it *now!* It also said I evaluate and discriminate and my mind is a finely tuned instrument for doing just that.

The author congratulated me for being a natural-born leader, full of courage, energy, and initiative, and went on to tell me I was basically a loner and fond of keeping my own counsel. He said trivia and detail appall me (actually, they bore me to tears).

The book warned that no matter how old I get, I will always retain my childlike eagerness to reach out and grasp that nearest to me; it further cautioned that if I ever lose this impulsive quality, I will lose something of myself.

Page 8 said I would be forever young psychologically, ennobled by my very own originality. The same page also revealed I was an open and honest person (sometimes so much so that it hurts), and a bad liar. (I'm not so sure about that; once in a while I tell a white one.) The author clearly stated that I have a tendency to be a "bit bossy," and anyone asking me for a favor will find it a very exhausting business. (Very true.)

Still on this page (the best one), it mentioned that on the surface I am friendly and communicative but don't encourage intimate relationships, and those who become my friends, in the truest sense, can indeed count themselves fortunate that I allow them within the inner circle of my life. A friend is more important to me than anything in the world, even above money and worldly possessions. (Few people will believe this, but it is true.)

Onward to page 9 and a paragraph that stated I work day and night to deliver that which I have promised.

I think there is no end to my reserves of energy, and when all is said and done, I am the outright winner: in the ulcer derby. (I have three.)

The last paragraph implied that I am incredibly self-confident, convinced I can do anything that appeals to me better than the next person. Experience is something an Aries person believes he was born with. (My mother believes this one hundred per cent.)

On a sad note, the book said I have a superpolyurethane, crack-resistant veneer that does not allow me to become hurt. (I think my mother contributed this one.)

When the book summed up all the characteristics, it concluded I was the type who, in the old Wild West days, would have accepted a gun duel and learned to shoot on the way to the appointment.

My mother said the person who wrote this book certainly had my number, and, by God, she was going to let him know she was into astrology from now on.

I didn't tell Mom this was only the good stuff, simply because there wasn't anything bad to relate.

Silence Is Golden??

When I was little my mother used to say, "Never speak to strangers, don't get in cars with someone you don't know, and don't ever take candy from strangers." I tell my kids the same thing every morning when they leave for school. To this day I hate it when strangers come up to me and try to start a conversation. I don't mind a comment on the weather because

I can nod to that, but there's always this fear that if I speak to someone, my mother will find out.

Several days ago I was waiting for a train in New York and trying unobtrusively to read a discarded *Playboy* magazine when a person sat down next to me. I say person because I'm still not sure if it was male, female, or an it. It's hard to tell when a person is wearing sixty-two pounds of jewelry and has shoulder-length hair. The pants tucked into knee-high boots offered no clues. The rhinestone-studded shirt and the yellow satin cape did nothing but blind me.

When I put on my sunglasses to ward off the glare, the individual asked if I had an astigmatism. I shook my head (it was one of those nod answers) and tried to figure out if the picture I was looking at was upside down or if the photographer had used a faulty camera.

I noted out of the corner of my eye that my seat companion was looking pointedly at the magazine I was trying to shield with my handbag, and asked me if I was liberated. Since I don't speak to strangers, and since I viewed the question as an invasion of privacy, I ignored him. He was a persistent little devil, I'll give him that, because he inched a little closer and repeated the question.

I looked around for some of New York City's finest and didn't see a one. The whole concourse was filled with senior citizens taking a trip to the Delaware Water Gap. I made sure my mother wasn't in evidence and gave him a steely glance (which was lost on him because of the sunglasses) and said I considered myself independent and not liberated. I also told him in order to be liberated, one had to be under an iron rule of thumb (in my opinion), so that when one extricated oneself, one could then appreciate being liberated. I then told him a liberated female was someone who had to burn her bra, and I had no intention of doing that because nobody would notice and then I would have to purchase new underwear, and if there was one thing I hated to do, it was to buy underwear.

My seat companion said, "Huh?"

I ignored him and continued to stare at the picture in *Playboy*. It was almost time for the train and I still hadn't figured out if the picture was upside down or not, and there was no way I was going to carry it on the train for the whole world to see. I was on my way to a permanent crick in the neck when the neon sign next to me said I must be a female chauvinist. Now, that really ticked me off, since I didn't know if he was animal, vegetable, or mineral. I took another look over my shoulder to be sure my mother wasn't in the geriatric set, removed my Gucci sunglasses, and blinked at his dazzling brilliance. I told him I was a hit man for the Mafia and if he didn't buzz off, I would squirt him with my gun that was full of Clorox.

The rainbow quirked his left eyebrow, threw the lemon-yellow cape over his shoulder with a flourish, and pleaded to be allowed to ask one more question.

"What?" I growled.

"Why are you looking at that picture upside down?" Then he glanced at an oldster passing by and said there was a lot of crazy people running around loose.

I threw the magazine at his retreating back and watched as it fell open to the centerfold. Mom would have been proud of me, I thought as I ran to catch my train.

Who Says Chivalry Is Dead?

I learned something the other day: you can't judge a book by its cover, and dogs really do have an uncanny instinct about people.

I exited the supermarket with my usual two carts full of groceries and plopped them in the back seat of the car. (The trunk is only used for basketballs, footballs, baseballs, bats, warm-up suits, and skateboards.)

My knowledge of cars extends only to being able to turn the key; it either goes or it doesn't. This one didn't.

I got out of the car and glanced around for a man who looked as if he would help a middle-aged lady with twenty paper bags and a dog. A man dressed in a suit and tie ignored me completely when I said, "Sir!" My dog went after his heels and the hair on her back bristled. Another man said he couldn't help me because he had to pick up his wife at the beauty parlor. Sam growled deep in her throat at his lack of interest. A third man said he took his cars to the garage and he knew even less than I did. My dog chased him all the way to the liquor store.

A little old lady carrying a load of potatoes stopped and let Samantha lick her hand. She told me to lift up the lid (that's what she said, lift up the lid) and bang the doohickey on top of the battery. Since I didn't have a hammer, the dog watched her potatoes while we banged the doohickey with a skateboard. When

171

the car wouldn't start, she told me to close the lid and call a taxi.

Another man went by, ignoring me completely when my dog growled and showed her teeth.

I was about to take Sam and my semi-melted ice cream and walk home when a van pulled alongside my car. A young man got out and looked at me and then at my dog. I gulped. He had hair down to his hips and tied back with a piece of twine. He also had an earring in one ear. His jeans had a million patches and he was barefoot. He sauntered over to me, a can of beer in his hand, and asked, "Are you having trouble, ma'am?"

I nodded.

"Hey, guys, this lady is having a problem," he shouted into the van. Three more just like him exited and looked at me. The dog was licking the foam from the top of the beer can and doing all kinds of tricks for attention.

Thirty minutes later they decided I had a dead battery. One of the kids said he would take me and my groceries home and come back and tow my car. My mother's words of "Don't speak to strangers" and my husband's ominous warnings about hippies and yippies that prey on innocent women ran through my mind. I looked at Sam, who was on her back having her belly scratched, and made up my mind. "You have to take my dog," I said.

They agreed. "You got it, lady," one of them said as I hopped in the van.

They carried all twenty bags of groceries into the house for me and took the dog with them when they went back for the car.

While they were gone, I called my husband and told him what had happened. I can't repeat what he said.

An hour later my car was in the driveway. I offered the kids some money and they refused. They did, however, take a bottle of grape juice and a package of Fig Newtons with them.

"Thanks again," I said.

"No sweat. In that get-up you didn't have a prayer," one of them remarked as he eyed my sneakers, blue jeans, and Edison Little League windbreaker. "Maybe one of these days your son will help my mother."

"You can count on it," I replied happily. Sam agreed.

I Can Read and I'm Programmed, Too!

Woman can not live by bread alone: she needs signs, especially this woman.

The first thing that greets me in the morning is a note taped on the bathroom mirror that clearly states, "Cleanliness is next to Godliness." It's good for two things. (1) You can't see what you look like, and (2) it reminds everyone to leave the bathroom the way he or she found it: a mess.

The indecision of what to prepare for breakfast gets a helping hand from a sign that reads, "You never know what you can do until you have to undo what you did."

My decision made, I schlep to the stove, where a wooden plaque tells me: "When in charge, ponder; when in trouble, delegate. When in doubt, mumble." And that's exactly what I do, mumble as I put on an apron carrying the message, "For this I spent four years in college???"

My apron tied, I reach for the toaster inside the

173

cabinet where I think I put it the last time, and see a sign that says, "I finally got it all together, but I forgot where I put it."

You have to admit this is a snappy way to begin each day.

Onward and upward to my office and a sign made by my son in his wood-working class. It says, "I'm too busy to be organized."

A small plastic sign given to me by some fool sits on my desk and reminds me that if everything is going well, I have obviously overlooked something.

Splashed across the top of my calendar is, "The years skip along easily, it's the days that are tough."

All of the above just proves I'm alive and can read. What really bothers me is, I think every housewife in America is programmed.

For example, when your entire family wakes up and everyone yells in unison that the sheets smell like April freshness.

Nobody got a whiter, brighter smile, and they put their money where their mouth was.

Somebody cries out that she can see herself in the breakfast dishes.

Somebody else says that the furniture polish lights up the whole house and we're ready for Grandma and the white-glove test.

One of the kids shouts that he washed one of his sweat socks in Clorox and the other in plain detergent. Both came out the same. A neighbor's kid says he should have put it in the Biz bag.

My daughter grumbles that she can't make up her mind if she should smell mediciney or soda-pop sweet.

The youngest is hysterical because the new soap didn't make him tingle from head to toe, and his glasses do so have gummy residue.

"Oh, my God," my husband babbles, "these glasses have spots on them. What are the neighbors going to think? Buy Cascade!" he orders imperiously as he heads out the door.

"I would," I yell back, "but I ignored the sign in my car that says, 'This car runs on gas, not fumes.' "

I, for One, Am Violently Opposed...

Our ten-year-old, David, came in from school the other day with a note saying a one hundred percent attendance was expected for a meeting to discuss violence on television.

My son watched me file it with my other junk. "You're copping out, huh?"

"Sort of," I mumbled.

"The teacher said if all the mothers come, she would give us each a Hershey Bar and the whole room gets a star on the door. If the fathers come, we each get a pack of Bubble Yum and an extra star on the door," he whined.

I tried to bribe him. "I'll give you fifty cents and you can get two of each. I hate meetings."

"The teacher said you would say that," he continued to whine.

"So all right, I'll go, but I get the Hershey Bar."

He agreed. His father should have been so amenable. I literally had to drag him along.

After we saluted the flag, and after we sang "The Star-Spangled Banner," and after all the ladies looked over one another's clothing, and after we had refreshments, and after each mother checked out the attendance with regard to Hershey Bars and Bubble Yum and gold stars, we got down to business.

The chairperson said she would take a hand vote

to see how many were in agreement that the violence on television was harmful.

"That lets you out," my husband hissed. "If you couldn't take a stand on the ERA and abortion, what are you going to vote now?"

"What should I do?" I whispered.

"Do what you always do. Vote yes and then vote no."

The chairperson got into a real tizzy when the vote didn't come out right. Everyone did the same thing I did.

"I'm going to ignore the vote," she said angrily, "and get to the shows that are the real offenders. *Baretta, Kojak, Police Woman,* and *Starsky and Hutch.*"

"Oh, my God, did you hear what she said? She wants to take off *Starsky and Hutch.* I won't be able to sleep on Saturday nights if she does that. I want to change my vote," I yelled, waving my hand in the air.

"She wants to get rid of Angie Dickinson," Mike bellowed as he, too, rose to change his vote. Everyone wanted to change his vote.

The chairperson ignored all of us as she droned on that we needed more shows like *Father Knows Best, Nanny and the Professor,* and the old *Donna Reed Show.*

A militant in the back said she would take it to the Supreme Court if *Kojak* were taken off the air.

"If they take off *Police Woman, Charlie's Angels* will be next," a heavyset man in front shouted hysterically.

A petrified father said his kids would blow up the house if *Baretta* went off the air.

Somebody's grandmother said she would hold a mass rally at the senior citizens' home if they took off *Starsky and Hutch.* I clapped her on the back while someone shouted, "Let's hear it for the senior citizens!"

A hostile individual in the middle of the room said he had to go into therapy when his family watched *Father Knows Best*. All the fathers agreed with him.

A long-haired father wearing one earring wanted to know if *Love Boat* was on the list of offending shows. No one answered him.

Along about this time the principal jumped on the desk and yelled for quiet. "We're losing sight of the reason we're here. It's the children we're concerned about. Do you want your children watching violence that can corrupt them? Right now, because of the violence on his show, Telly Savalas is being sued. We have to make up our minds and take a stand."

The grandmother roared, "Horsefeathers!" She went on to say that any baldheaded man who sucked lollipops and was kind to old ladies had her vote.

An agitated mother shouted that she would send her kids to bed with the chickens, but she wasn't giving up her television for a bunch of hysterical people.

A radical standing near the door (for a quick exit, I'm sure) made a motion to lynch the chairperson and the principal.

A sweet young thing, who said she was standing in for her next-door neighbor who was out protesting something or other about the Panama Canal, declared that the solution was so obvious we all had overlooked it. She was wrong; every man had his eyes glued to her very obvious thirty-six-twenty-four-thirty-six frame; they panted for her next words. She said all we had to do was write a letter to the networks demanding time changes for the shows with violence. She also stated she would be willing, even though she had no children in the school system, to form a committee, and who would like to volunteer? Every man in the room almost killed himself getting in line.

The principal, who was rubbing his neck, called it an admirable suggestion and went to the head of the line to sign up.

177

I listened to the grandmother tell the radical standing near the door that she had only stopped by for the refreshments, and if she had known they were serving butterscotch cookies, she would have stayed home. The radical shrugged and invited her out for a drink.

The Front Porch

On my vacation this year I met an old friend I hadn't seen in over seventeen years. It took us an hour to lie to each other and say how great the other looked and how neither of us had changed at all and, if anything, we didn't get older, just better.

"What's the one thing you miss most about back home?" my friend asked.

I really had to think about it for a minute. "Probably the front porch. Remember how we used to sit on the wicker chairs, read Nancy Drew, drink lemonade, and stuff ourselves with brownies?"

She grinned. "Yeah. And remember how we used to look through the bamboo blind at the boys going by, feeling so smart because we could see them but they couldn't see us?"

"Now when I go home, I sit out there reading Mom's copy of *Tobacco Road,* eating dry roasted nuts so my blood pressure won't go up, and drinking Harvey Wallbangers. It's not the same," I grumbled.

"That's because all the boys got old," my friend said. She leaned over, a wild look in her eye, and whispered, "I have anxiety attacks."

"What's an anxiety attack?"

"Don't you get them?"

"What is it? Maybe we call it something else in New Jersey," I said, watching her carefully.

"You know. You hit the skids. All the kids are gone and the nest is empty. You mean you really don't get them? My psychiatrist said every woman over forty gets them."

"Oh, sure, at least three times a day. After a while you learn to live with them. In New Jersey we call them nervous fits."

"Swear to God that you'll never tell anyone I get them," she pleaded.

"I swear to God, hope to die, stick a finger in my eye," I said, making the sign of the cross on my chest. "My lips are sealed."

"Are you sure you'll never tell a soul?"

"Of course not," I said indignantly, "even though I think it's something the entire world should know. I tell anyone who will listen about my nervous fits. Do you get your anxiety attacks because you don't have a front porch?"

"Yeah, at least that's what the psychiatrist said. I have a patio in front and one in back. I don't have wicker furniture; I have wrought iron, and it's uncomfortable as hell. When it rains, everything gets wet. I hate it!" she cried fretfully.

"Is he helping you? Are you sure all this is because you don't have a front porch? I get anxiety attacks when the dog throws up on the carpet or the kids punch one another out at dinnertime."

"Absolutely. What other reason could there be?"

"Considering your age, a number of things; one being the big M."

"Never! It's because I don't have a front porch."

"Build one, and it will solve your problem."

"And have everyone in the neighborhood think I flaked out? I have to learn to live without having one or a bamboo blind. I have to conquer this problem."

179

"You're pushing forty-seven, so you better get a bead on it. You don't have a hell of a lot of time left. What's this psychiatrist doing for you besides taking your money?"

"He's not taking my money, he's doing it for free. I'm a test case."

"If the A.M.A. ever finds out, you're in trouble. They frown on freebies; doctors get a bad name from that kind of thing. Are you sure he's qualified?"

"Of course I am," she snorted indignantly. "He just started his practice and I'm his first patient."

"Some people put a coat of arms on their front door. A psychiatrist who lives two houses away from me hangs an inkblot on his. Is your shrink nutsy-cuckoo like that? What exactly is he doing for you? Can you pin it down?"

"I put birds in a nest."

"That's it, huh? You put birds in a nest," I said, inching away.

"Not exactly. He takes you into a room that is a simulated woodsy playground for birds. On the middle of the table is this gigantic birds' nest. I put birds in it. All kinds of birds, all different sizes. They're made out of plastic and have feathers glued to them."

"What's the nest made of?"

"Plastic. You know the kind we used to use to make belts and wallets when we were at camp. I pick out the birds that are bothering me and place them in strategic spots in the nest, according to my mood. For instance, if one of my friends is annoying me, I make her a bird and put her in the nest. I can throw her out if I want to; the choice is mine. Wherever I place her is how important she is to me. Then I talk about it. Last week I didn't put any birds in the nest at all, because no one was important to me."

"God, that's terrible. And all because you don't have a front porch! Listen, I don't think there's anything wrong with you. Take my advice and get rid of of your shrink. I think he's off the wall."

"Not any longer. He was in therapy for a while, but he's all better now. Weaving the birds' nest is what cured him."

The Secret

For some people a secret is something that just has to be told. To other people it's a tool to use to drive someone insane. For example, I know something so terrible, so horrendous, you'll just die if I tell you. Or, I know something about you-know-who, but I promised not to tell. And then there is the keeper of the best secret in the whole world. Arthur Treacher and his famous batter recipe.

I have a friend who went so far as to apply for a job at the chippery and was turned down. They told her they only hired kids, their reasoning being that young minds cannot be corrupted.

A neighbor of mine hired a chemist to analyze the cooked batter. He charged her thirty-five dollars and told her the hot oil broke down the ingredients and he couldn't tell what was what.

My ears almost blocked up the day I heard a woman say she would do "anything" for the formula.

My eyeballs almost fell out of my head the time I saw a little old lady grab the youth behind the counter, shouting that she needed the recipe so she could die happy.

Another time I overheard a man, who made his living by fishing, offer to supply the store with free fish for a whole year if they would just part with the batter's contents.

Just a couple of days ago I heard a young mother with two toddlers beg for the secret, telling the girl behind the counter that her kids wouldn't eat anything but Arthur's fish, and wouldn't the girl please, just this once, give it to her. She would never tell a soul, not even her own mother. When her pleas were refused, she left her children sitting in the booth and went home . . . alone.

I myself would give my right arm and left foot for the recipe, but would never resort to anything so ridiculous. What I did was threaten to kill myself if they didn't give it to me. When they didn't give in, I went back to my seat and ate my food.

The day Arthur went to the big fish fry in the sky, the store was jammed with expectant people who thought that if ever there was a time for sharing and generosity, this was it.

The local news station interrupted its daily program to announce that despite the riots, the accidents, the fist fights, and the obscene language, the secret of the batter was still intact.

The White Lie

If you were to take a poll and ask people if they ever tell a lie, even a little white one, they'll look you in the eye, lie, and say no. I tried it and was amazed at the number of truthful people in this world, of which I am not one.

I've been known to spin out a few from time to time. For instance:

182

I tell the paperboy I don't have any change, so my husband will have to pay him on Saturday.

I never tell my friends my eyelashes cost seven dollars and fifty cents when they compliment me on how thick and curly they are. (In my opinion, not saying anything is the same as telling a lie.)

Every time the Avon lady calls, I tell her I just bought one of everything from my niece who is also an Avon lady.

I constantly tell the mailman my dog doesn't have teeth.

I called up the Auto Club and told them vandals dented my car, so that I wouldn't have to pay the one hundred dollar deductible.

I told the telephone repairman the dog chewed through the wire, when I really cut it myself to save my sanity.

I called up David's teacher and told her my kid would never, never, under any circumstance, glue a frog to her chair.

I notified the gas company that I smelled a leak so they would come and fix the pilot light, because I didn't want to crawl behind the furnace.

I told my friend her new dress looked terrible, knowing she would take it back and then I could buy it, since it would look better on me.

When Mike complimented me on dinner, I didn't share the honors with Swanson.

Barely Entertaining

Did you ever tell someone something, and three days later, when the story gets back to you, it is barely recognizable?

A while ago I read an article from the AP Service that said a twenty-five-year-old blonde woman, beautifully curved, streaked down the length of a DC-10 into the no-frills section of a National airliner bound for Los Angeles. It also stated that the lovely lady cavorted up and down the aisles, finally perching herself atop row twenty-seven to guzzle champagne before the crew managed to capture her and wrap a blanket around her.

A spokesman for the airline later commented that "it did happen, but it is not part of our standard inflight entertainment. We intend to stick with movies and stereo."

Three days later, while standing at the checkout counter of the supermarket, I heard a group of people discussing the article.

One very verbal gentleman, who had a grin as wide as the Grand Canyon, said the pilot put the plane on automatic and asked to see a replay.

A nutsy-cuckoo, buying three cases of pork and beans, commented that he heard all the people wearing Fruit of the Loom underwear went bananas.

A militant, eating a popsicle he had no intention of paying for, stated that the plane circled the airport forty-five times before it landed. When it did, the ghost of Flight 51 scampered from the plane, waving her champagne bottle, yelling she had just inherited five million dollars. He said he should know, he was there.

My very own husband noted there was a line a mile long outside the travel agency and that National was booked solid for the next six months. He said everyone loves unadvertised entertainment.

Truth in Advertising

I have a friend who works for a consumer group that answers questions about certain products on the market. She said these were questions that every woman wants to ask but is afraid to.

1. Will control-top panty hose work for a figure out of control? Who decides when a figure is out of control?

2. If I lock the bathroom door when I use an aerosol hair spray, will it harm the ozone layer? Will I die from the fumes?

3. Is there something wrong with a person if she doesn't laugh when she uses a deodorant that is supposed to make you laugh? I only laugh when my boyfriend tickles me under the arms. Rush your reply in a plain brown wrapper.

4. Can you use Dorothy's shampoo if you don't ice-skate? I have weak ankles.

5. I bought a moisturizer that said my face would drink up moisture. What should I do if my cheeks get fat from all the excess drinking?

6. Recently I purchased a shampoo that promised my hair would get excited if I used it. Two things happened. The first time I used it my hair became so

excited it fainted and hung limply. The second time my hair became so excited the ends split. Please advise.

7. I received a free sample of mascara in the mail. It said my lashes would get fat if I used it. If this happens, do you put them on Weight Watchers, and does it really work?

8. I've been thinking about buying a certain perfume advertised on television that claims, "If you want to get his attention, whisper." Does this mean I do the whispering or does the perfume? What happens if the person you're whispering to is hard of hearing?

9. The label on a bottle of hand lotion states that if I use it, my hands will become petal-soft. Petals fall off. Do you have a remedy for this condition?

10. I bought a bottle of hair color because the commercial convinced me "I was worth it." Who else will know besides me? If I'm going to spend all that money, I want everyone to know I'm worth it. I want to dye my hair on Friday, so could you answer this right away?

When I asked my friend what kind of answers they gave to questions such as these, she said they had a standard answer for all of them.

There is truth and untruth in advertising.

One of a Kind

Whoever it was that said the universal language is love was wrong—it's slang. Most people think of themselves as being distinctive, unique, one of a kind. They harbor this illusion until they open their mouths, at which point everyone seems to sound alike.

Just the other day I listened to a group of neighbors speaking on a variety of subjects. All I got out of the conversation was nine "Oh, for God's sakes," eight "I don't believe this" (usually accompanied by a quirked eyebrow), eleven "This is the pits," and five "You know what you can tell that . . ." (delivered with a mandatory sneer).

The following are some occasions when you can use one or all of these particular expressions. Rarely can one use more than two in one sentence, but anything is possible.

1. Your guaranteed smokeless self-clean oven creates a thick gray cloud throughout the entire house.

2. Somebody hooks up the garden hose to a leaky faucet in the kitchen.

3. The Roto Rooter man says, "That will be sixty-five dollars. Next time just jiggle the handle."

4. The bathroom scale makes you gain five pounds overnight.

5. The tassel from the plant hanger gets caught in the garbage disposal and the kitchen ceiling falls down.

6. If you insist on riding the clutch, you know it's a whole new gear shift.

7. Yogurt is for zits, but sex is better, so says one husband.

8. Letters from the teacher written in green crayon that say your son is doing well in math.

9. But I have a whole side of beef in the freezer; it can't be broken.

10. The bank says the check you mailed to your in-laws bounced.

As I said, it's rare that you can use more than one of these nifty little phrases in one sentence, but I managed the other day when I was returning from Washington. The plane was over two hours late and I was last in line to board. When a stewardess tells you that you forgot your boarding pass, and the pilot is ready to take off, what would you say?

How about: "Oh, for God's sake, this is the pits. Don't you think this is a bit heavy? You can see I have a ticket. You know what you can tell that pilot, don't you!"

She told him, and I took the train home.

Going Up in Smoke

Every year when the storm windows go up, my husband starts to harp on his favorite subject: quit smoking!

I tried everything and nothing worked. I chewed gum and when it stuck to the filter, I still couldn't quit. I have to admit it was rather like sucking on an egg, but I still couldn't give up my security blanket.

Once I clipped a magazine article written by a well-known doctor that suggested taking a cold shower and drinking a glass of orange juice every time you craved a cigarette. In a single day I made the water company and Anita Bryant rich.

The day the storm windows went up this year, I knew Mike meant business when he stomped into the house snapping and snarling that he needed a Seeing Eye dog to get through the smoke. Then he said he had enrolled me in a Smoker's Clinic. The fee was twenty-five dollars and the brochure said you smoked while you quit. What could be better? I joined.

The first meeting started off with the instructor telling us he didn't use scare tactics. He then proceeded to quote death statistics and X-rayed our lungs. He told us if we wanted to smoke while we were being X-rayed, to go right ahead. I went right ahead. After the X-rays he assigned us each a number. I was quittee twenty-three. He said that in the hereafter, if there was one, we would be referred to by our individual quittee numbers.

The second meeting was great. When the instructor started showing the members their X-rays, quittee nineteen passed out. The instructor informed us the woman just fainted. Maybe that's what he thought, but I knew she had died. That was when I quit. Besides, I hated it when my husband called me quittee twenty-three.

I was back to running up our water bill and making Anita Bryant richer, when my husband came up with another plan. Mike thought I should pretend to smoke a straw. Most people don't know that plastic burns, and blisters on the end of one's nose take forever to heal.

The next program was the one that worked. He came in from work one day and peered deeply into my eyes and said, "I see you aren't dead yet." Then Mike started waking me up at three A.M., whispering in my ear, "You're going to bite the dust and I'm going to spend all your money on my new wife. We'll use your Lenox dishes with the strawberries for everyday, and those twenty dollar bath towels you've been saving for the Queen of England's visit."

He kept it up for thirty days, scaring the hell out of me. It got to the point where I was waking up ahead of him, just waiting for his ominous words of doom. Once I had to wake him up and tell him to get on with it.

It wasn't until I was a bona-fide quittee some six

weeks later that I realized I didn't have any twenty dollar bath towels, and how far would he and his new wife get on my seven dollars and thirty-nine cents?

Just What I Always Wanted

The aftermath of Christmas is such a letdown that conversation, like everything else, seems to lag. This year one of our neighbors deliberately threw a party so we could discuss the ridiculous and worthless gifts we got. She went so far as to offer two of her prize Captain Marvel comic books for the most worthless gift.

Joan Knight started off by telling us she got a Hammacher Schlemmer aquarium. We had twenty minutes of ripe conversation: (1) Three hundred dollars and no water and fish! (2) Who the hell is Hammacher Schlemmer? (3) And you say a good friend gave it to you! (4) What do you mean you just stare at a Hammacher Schlemmer?

Paula Sachs extolled the virtues of her Drink Maid Mixer, a bikini doll that mixes your drink while she shakes and grates. The conversation that followed was too risque and pornographic to mention, but it lasted forty-five minutes.

Ann Witt got a paper shredder. We all oohed and aahed, since she was the first one on the street to get one. She said she shredded napkins for three days and spent seven dollars on waste paper just so she could tell her mother-in-law that she used it.

Stan Laird received an IOU from some anonymous person for a nature environment box that would allow him to sit and "enjoy spring showers, warm ambiance,

Chinook winds, Baja sun, tropical rain, and jungle steam." He said he wasn't going to share it with anyone, even his wife, because it was such a personal item. Even though he didn't have the gift in his hand, he said it qualified him for the two Captain Marvel comic books.

His wife, Pat, pushed him out the door, yelling something that sounded like, "I'll give you Baja sun and Chinook winds when I get home!"

My husband, who was standing closest to Stan, told us that wasn't what she said at all.

Diane Anderson got a Newtonian Nutcracker that works by putting a steel ball in a cylinder and dropping it on top of the nut. We spent an hour discussing Captain Queeg and how it beat cracking nuts with your heel.

Al Gretz laid claim to a fifty-seven-inch Pepper Mill that stands on the floor. He said it weighed eighty-seven pounds and you had to nail it to the ground. After an hour of serious discussion we all agreed it was probably supposed to be used as a coat rack for midgets.

I got a gift, and I think you'll agree, for the woman who has everything. A pair of gold electroplated egg scissors. What this little gem does is snip off the top of hard-boiled eggs. I'll never know how I lived before I got this fantastic implement.

Good sport that I am, I shared one of the comic books with Stan. He took it graciously and said he would allow me to share some of his tropical rain and jungle steam when the nature box arrived.

Love by Any Other Name

"A one-question test and you got an F! Explain, please," I requested of my middle daughter.

"The teacher only gave us ten minutes to answer the test, but she's giving us another chance to make up the grade. You have to take the exam, and if you put down a good answer I'll pass," Patty said, throwing her test paper on the table.

" 'What is love?' Hold it! Are you telling me this is the one-question test?"

"You got it! I need your answer by tomorrow morning."

"Look, you don't just rattle off an answer to a question like that. I'll need at least a three-day extension."

"Try telling that to the teacher. I said love was liking someone a lot. She said that was the lousiest answer she had ever heard of, and she said she was ashamed of me because my mother was a writer. She hates me, Mom! She hates writers!"

It was three forty-five P.M. when I started on my assignment. At eleven thirty-six P.M., while everyone else was in bed, I was still staring at a blank piece of paper.

"You said you were a writer," my husband observed, sleepily.

"I am, I am. What's your definition of love?"

"Liking someone a lot."

"It figures."

I called two of my friends. Joan said love was an endurance test. Pat said love was either-or.

192

"Either-or? What kind of answer is that? What does it mean?"

"Cuddling in bed. Either with your husband or someone else."

"God, I can't use that answer."

"Then don't call me at midnight and ask me crazy questions," she retorted.

It was three thirty-three in the A.M. when I dialed my mother and asked her the same question. After she told me I was as flaky as my sister Dory, she said love was survival of the fittest. I told her to wake up Dad and ask him the same question. He said love was peace and quiet at three thirty-three in the morning.

At seven-twenty I wrote my answer on a piece of paper. Love is understanding and giving the other person room to grow.

Predictions

Mike told me, now that I was a columnist, I should make predictions like everyone else.

"I don't even know what pair of blue jeans I'll be wearing tomorrow or how I'll comb my hair," I complained. "How can I make predictions if I can't make up my mind?"

My husband said you win a few and you lose a few, and a year from now no one will remember what I predicted.

"How about if I just guess?"

My husband said to go right ahead.

I sat down with pencil and paper and pondered and thought. Thought and pondered. "How about this one?

193

Billy.Carter will make a fortune this year on his beer commercials. I'll be vague and say millions—how's that?"

My husband nodded and said it was good for starters.

"Monday-night football is here to stay, and every wife in these United States will buy a nightgown made from Astro Turf."

"Now you got it," Mike chortled happily.

Flushed with success, I continued. "The price of candy will skyrocket during Easter."

"Hardly a biggie, but okay."

"The kids of America will go back to shooting marbles as the all-American pastime.

"Sex will be the number-two pastime."

"Oh, my God, don't get carried away!" my husband cried. "What's going to be number one?"

"Skateboarding."

"But you just said marbles was going to be the all-American pastime."

"Right, right, but that's for kids. Sex is for people like us."

"Yes, but what's going to be number one?" he asked fretfully.

"How should I know? What's wrong with skateboarding?"

"It will never replace sex, I can tell you that."

"It's skateboarding," I said firmly.

"You need one more, a real zinger."

"How about, 'Art Buchwald is going to run for President, and Jack Anderson will be his running mate. They promise, if elected, to take all our money and give each person an allowance.' Who's going to remember, three years from now, that I was the one who predicted it?"

"Jack Anderson will remember. Why don't you have Anderson run for President and Buchwald be his running mate?"

"You got it! Do you think I'll get an award or something for these predictions?"

"Or something," Mike said, snapping my pencil in two.